MY DEAR STAIR,

      We have travelled so many roads together, highland and lowland, pleasant and dreary, that I ask you to accept this book of travellers' tales. For Scotland is a wide place to travel in for those who believe that it is not bounded strictly by kirk and market-place, and who have an ear for old songs and lost romances. It is of the back-world of Scotland that I write, the land behind the mist and over the seven bens, a place hard of access for the foot-passenger but easy for the maker of stories. Meantime, to you, who have chosen the better part, I wish many bright days by hill and loch in the summers to come.

J B.

R.M.S. *Briton, at sea.*
   September 1901.

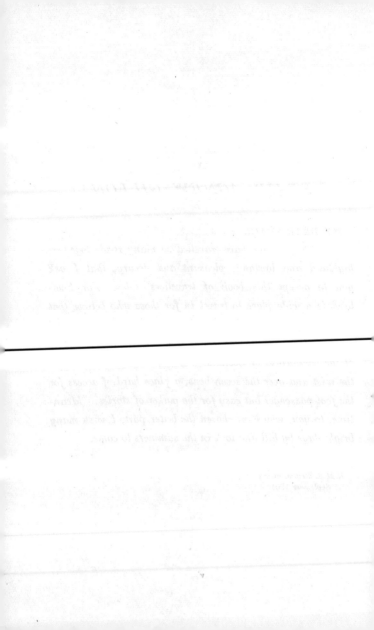

CONTENTS

I

NO-MAN'S-LAND

NO-MAN'S-LAND

CHAPTER I

THE SHIELING OF FARAWA

IT was with a light heart and a pleasing consciousness of holiday that I set out from the
inn at Allermuir to tramp my fifteen miles into
the unknown. I walked slowly, for I carried my
equipment on my back—my basket, fly-books and
rods, my plaid of Grant tartan (for I boast myself
a kinsman of that house), and my great staff,
which had tried ere then the front of the steeper
Alps. A small valise with books and some changes
of linen clothing had been sent on ahead in the
shepherd's own hands. It was yet early April, and
before me lay four weeks of freedom—twenty-eight
blessed days in which to take fish and smoke the
pipe of idleness. The Lent term had pulled me
down, a week of modest enjoyment thereafter in
town had finished the work ; and I drank in the
sharp moorish air like a thirsty man who has been
forwandered among deserts.

I am a man of varied tastes and a score of
interests. As an undergraduate I had been filled

with the old mania for the complete life. I distinguished myself in the Schools, rowed in my college eight, and reached the distinction of practising for three weeks in the Trials. I had dabbled in a score of learned activities, and when the time came that I won the inevitable St. Chad's fellowship on my chaotic acquirements, and I found myself compelled to select if I would pursue a scholar's life, I had some toil in finding my vocation. In the end I resolved that the ancient life of the North, of the Celts and the Northmen and the unknown Pictish tribes, held for me the chief fascination. I had acquired a smattering of Gaelic, having been brought up as a boy in Lochaber, and now I set myself to increase my store of languages. I mastered Icelandic, and my first book—a monograph on the probable Celtic elements in the Eddic songs—brought me the praise of scholars and the deputy-professor's chair of Northern Antiquities. So much for Oxford. My vacations had been spent mainly in the North—in Ireland, Scotland, and the Isles, in Scandinavia and Iceland, once even in the far limits of Finland. I was a keen sportsman of a sort, an old-experienced fisher, a fair shot with gun and rifle, and in my hillcraft I might well stand comparison with most men. April has ever seemed to me the finest season of the year even in our cold northern altitudes, and the memory of many bright Aprils had brought me up from the South on the night before to Allerfoot, whence a dog-cart had taken me up Glen Aller to the inn at Allermuir; and now the same desire had set me on the heather with my face to the cold brown hills.

You are to picture a sort of plateau, benty and rock-strewn, running ridgewise above a chain of little peaty lochs and a vast tract of inexorable bog. In a mile the ridge ceased in a shoulder of hill, and over this lay the head of another glen, with the same doleful accompaniment of sunless lochs, mosses, and a tortuous water. East and west and north, in every direction save the south, rose walls of gashed and serrated hills. It was a grey day with blinks of sun, and when a ray chanced to fall on one of the great dark faces, lines of light and colour sprang into being which told of mica and granite. I was in high spirits, as on the eve of holiday; I had breakfasted excellently on eggs and salmon steaks; I had no cares to speak of, and my prospects were not uninviting. But in spite of myself the landscape began to take me in thrall and crush me. The silent vanished peoples of the hills seemed to be stirring; dark primeval faces seemed to stare at me from behind boulders and jags of rock. The place was so still, so free from the cheerful clamour of nesting birds, that it seemed a *temenos* sacred to some old-world god. At my feet the lochs lapped ceaselessly; but the waters were so dark that one could not see bottom a foot from the edge. On my right the links of green told of snake-like mires waiting to crush the unwary wanderer. It seemed to me for the moment a land of death, where the tongues of the dead cried aloud for recognition.

My whole morning's walk was full of such fancies. I lit a pipe to cheer me, but the things would not be got rid of. I thought of the Gaels who had held those fastnesses; I thought of the Britons before them, who yielded to their advent. They were all strong peoples in their day, and now they had gone the way of the earth. They had left their mark on the levels of the glens and on the more habitable uplands, both in names and in actual forts, and graves where men might still dig curios. But the hills—that black stony amphitheatre before me—it seemed strange that the hills bore no traces of them. And then with some uneasiness I reflected on that older and stranger race who were said to have held the hilltops. The Picts, the Picti—what in the name of goodness were they? They had troubled me in all my studies, a sort of blank wall to put an end to speculation. We knew nothing of them save certain strange names which men called Pictish, the names of those hills in front of me—the Muneraw, the Yirnie, the Calmarton. They were the *corpus vile* for learned experiment; but Heaven alone knew what dark abyss of savagery once yawned in the midst of this desert.

And then I remembered the crazy theories of a pupil of mine at St. Chad's, the son of a small landowner on the Aller, a young gentleman who had spent his substance too freely at Oxford, and was now dreeing his weird in the Backwoods. He had been no scholar; but a certain imagination marked all his doings, and of a Sunday night he would come and talk to me of the North. The Picts were his special subject, and his ideas were mad. "Listen to me," he would say, when I had mixed him toddy and given him one of my cigars; "I believe there are traces—ay, and more than traces—of an old culture lurking in those hills and waiting to be discovered. We never hear of the Picts being driven from the hills. The Britons drove them from the lowlands, the Gaels from Ireland did the same for the Britons; but the hills were left unmolested. We hear of no one going near them except outlaws and tinklers. And in that very place you have the strangest mythology. Take the story of the Brownie. What is that but the story of a little swart man of uncommon strength and cleverness, who does good and ill indiscriminately, and then disappears? There are many scholars, as you yourself confess, who think that the origin of the Brownie was in some mad belief in the old race of the Picts, which still survived somewhere in the hills. And do we not hear of the Brownie in authentic records right down to the year 1756? After that, when people grew more incredulous, it is natural that the belief should have begun to die out; but I do not see why stray traces should not have survived till late."

"Do you not see what that means?" I had said in mock gravity. "Those same hills are, if anything, less known now than they were a hun-

dred years ago. Why should not your Picts or
Brownies be living to this day ? "

" Why not, indeed ? " he had rejoined, in all
seriousness.

I laughed, and he went to his rooms and returned with a large leather-bound book. It was
lettered, in the rococo style of a young man's
taste, *Glimpses of the Unknown*, and some of the
said glimpses he proceeded to impart to me. It
was not pleasant reading ; indeed, I had rarely
heard anything so well fitted to shatter sensitive
nerves. The early part consisted of folk-tales and
folk-sayings, some of them wholly obscure, some
of them with a glint of meaning, but all of them
with some hint of a mystery in the hills. I heard
the Brownie story in countless versions. Now the
thing was a friendly little man, who wore grey
breeches and lived on brose ; now he was a twisted
being, the sight of which made the ewes miscarry
in the lambing time. But the second part was
the stranger, for it was made up of actual tales,
most of them with date and place appended. It
was a most Bedlamite catalogue of horrors, which,
if true, made the wholesome moors a place instinct
with tragedy. Some told of children carried away
from villages, even from towns, on the verge of
the uplands. In almost every case they were
girls, and the strange fact was their utter disappearance. Two little girls would be coming
home from school, would be seen last by a neigh-
bour just where the road crossed a patch of heath
or entered a wood and then—no human eye ever

uplifted crook—"see that sicht. Is that no what is written of in the Bible when it says, 'The mountains do smoke'?" And with this piece of exegesis he finished his talk, and in a little we were at the cottage.

It was a small enough dwelling in truth, and yet large for a moorland house, for it had a garret below the thatch, which was given up to my sole enjoyment. Below was the wide kitchen with box-beds, and next to it the inevitable second room, also with its cupboard sleeping-places. The interior was very clean, and yet I remember to have been struck with the faint musty smell which is inseparable from moorland dwellings. The kitchen pleased me best, for there the great rafters were black with peat reek, and the uncovered stone floor, on which the fire gleamed dully, gave an air of primeval simplicity. But the walls spoiled all, for tawdry things of to-day had penetrated even there. Some grocers' almanacs—years old—hung in places of honour, and an extraordinary lithograph of the Royal Family in its youth. And this between crooks and fishing-rods and old guns, and horns of sheep and deer.

The life for the first day or two was regular and placid. I was up early, breakfasted on porridge (a dish which I detest), and then off to the lochs and streams. At first my sport prospered mightily. With a drake-wing I killed a salmon of seventeen pounds, and the next day had a fine basket of trout from a hill burn. Then for no earthly reason the weather changed. A bitter wind came out of the north-east, bringing showers of snow and stinging hail, and lashing the waters into storm. It was now farewell to fly-fishing. For a day or two I tried trolling with the minnow on the lochs, but it was poor sport, for I had no boat, and the edges were soft and mossy. Then in disgust I gave up the attempt, went back to the cottage, lit my biggest pipe, and sat down with a book to await the turn of the weather.

The shepherd was out from morning till night at his work, and when he came in at last, dog-tired, his face would be set and hard, and his eyes heavy with sleep. The strangeness of the man grew upon me. He had a shrewd brain beneath his thatch of hair, for I had tried him once or twice, and found him abundantly intelligent. He had some smattering of an education, like all Scottish peasants, and, as I have said, he was deeply religious. I set him down as a fine type of his class, sober, serious, keenly critical, free from the bondage of superstition. But I rarely saw him, and our talk was chiefly in monosyllables—short interjected accounts of the number of lambs dead or alive on the hill. Then he would produce a pencil and note-book, and be immersed in some calculation; and finally he would be revealed sleeping heavily in his chair, till his sister wakened him, and he stumbled off to bed.

So much for the ordinary course of life; but one day—the second, I think, of the bad weather

—the extraordinary happened. The storm had passed in the afternoon into a resolute and blinding snow, and the shepherd, finding it hopeless on the hill, came home about three o'clock. I could make out from his way of entering that he was in a great temper. He kicked his feet savagely against the door-post. Then he swore at his dogs, a thing I had never heard him do before. "Hell!" he cried, "can ye no keep out o' my road, ye bruits?" Then he came sullenly into the kitchen, thawed his numbed hands at the fire, and sat down to his meal.

I made some aimless remark about the weather.

"Death to man and beast," he grunted. "I hae got the sheep doun frae the hill, but the lambs will never thole this. We maun pray that it will no last."

His sister came in with some dish. "Margit," he cried, "three lambs away this morning, and three deid wi' the hole in the throat."

The woman's face visibly paled. "Guid help us, Adam; that hasna happened this three year."

"It has happened noo," he said surlily. "But, by God! if it happens again I'll gang mysel' to the Scarts o' the Muneraw."

"O Adam!" the woman cried shrilly, "haud your tongue. Ye kenna wha hears ye." And with a frightened glance at me she left the room.

I asked no questions, but waited till the shepherd's anger should cool. But the cloud did not pass so lightly. When he had finished his dinner he pulled his chair to the fire and sat staring moodily. He made some sort of apology to me for his conduct. "I'm sore troubled, sir; but I'm vexed ye should see me like this. Maybe things will be better the morn." And then, lighting his short black pipe, he resigned himself to his meditations.

But he could not keep quiet. Some nervous unrest seemed to have possessed the man. He got up with a start and went to the window, where the snow was drifting unsteadily past. As he stared out into the storm I heard him mutter to himself, "Three away, God help me, and three wi' the hole in the throat."

Then he turned round to me abruptly. I was jotting down notes for an article I contemplated in the *Revue Celtique*, so my thoughts were far away from the present. The man recalled me by demanding fiercely, "Do ye believe in God?"

I gave him some sort of answer in the affirmative.

"Then do ye believe in the Devil?" he asked.

The reply must have been less satisfactory, for he came forward and flung himself violently into the chair before me.

"What do ye ken about it?" he cried. "You that bides in a southern toun, what can ye ken o' the God that works in thae hills and the Devil —ay, the manifold devils—that He suffers to bide here? I tell ye, man, that if ye had seen what I have seen ye wad be on your knees at this moment praying to God to pardon your unbelief. There are devils at the back o' every stane and

hidin' in every cleuch, and it's by the grace o'
God alone that a man is alive upon the earth."
His voice had risen high and shrill, and then suddenly he cast a frightened glance towards the
window and was silent.

I began to think that the man's wits were un-
hinged, and the thought did not give me satisfaction. I had no relish for the prospect of being
left alone in this moorland dwelling with the
cheerful company of a maniac. But his next
movements reassured me. He was clearly only
dead-tired, for he fell sound asleep in his chair,
and by the time his sister brought tea and wakened
him, he seemed to have got the better of his excitement.

When the window was shuttered and the lamp
lit, I set myself again to the completion of my
notes. The shepherd had got out his Bible, and
was solemnly reading with one great finger travelling down the lines. He was smoking, and when-
ever some text came home to him with power
he would make pretence to underline it with the
end of the stem. Soon I had finished the work I
desired, and, my mind being full of my pet hobby,
I fell into an inquisitive mood, and began to question the solemn man opposite on the antiquities
of the place.

He stared stupidly at me when I asked him
concerning monuments or ancient weapons.

"I kenna," said he. "There's a heap o' queer
things in the hills."

"This place should be a centre for such relics.

You know that the name of the hill behind the house, as far as I can make it out, means the 'Place of the Little Men.' It is a good Gaelic word, though there is some doubt about its exact interpretation. But clearly the Gaelic peoples did not speak of themselves when they gave the name; they must have referred to some older and stranger population."

The shepherd looked at me dully, as not understanding.

"It is partly this fact—besides the fishing, of course—which interests me in this countryside," said I gaily.

Again he cast the same queer frightened glance towards the window. "If ye'll tak the advice of an aulder man," he said slowly, "ye'll let well alane and no meddle wi' uncanny things."

I laughed pleasantly, for at last I had found out my hard-headed host in a piece of childishness. "Why, I thought that you of all men would be free from superstition."

"What do ye call supersteetion?" he asked.

"A belief in old wives' tales," said I, "a trust in the crude supernatural and the patently impossible."

He looked at me beneath his shaggy brows. "How do ye ken what is impossible? Mind ye, sir, ye're no in the toun just now, but in the thick of the wild hills."

"But, hang it all, man," I cried, "you don't mean to say that you believe in that sort of thing? I am prepared for many things up here, but not

CHAPTER III

THE SCARTS OF THE MUNERAW

THE next morning was fine, for the snow had been intermittent, and had soon melted except in the high corries. True, it was deceptive weather, for the wind had gone to the rainy south-west, and the masses of cloud on that horizon boded ill for the afternoon. But some days' inaction had made me keen for a chance of sport, so I rose with the shepherd and set out for the day.

He asked me where I proposed to begin.

I told him the tarn called the Loch o' the Threshes, which lies over the back of the Muneraw on another watershed. It is on the ground of the Rhynns Forest, and I had fished it of old from the Forest House. I knew the merits of the trout, and I knew its virtues in a south-west wind, so I had resolved to go thus far afield.

The shepherd heard the name in silence. " Your best road will be ower that rig, and syne on to the water o' Caulds. Keep abune the moss till ye come to the place they ca' the Nick o' the Threshes. That will take ye to the very lochside, but it's a lang road and a sair."

The morning was breaking over the bleak hills. Little clouds drifted athwart the corries, and wisps of haze fluttered from the peaks. A great rosy flush lay over one side of the glen, which caught the edge of the sluggish bog pools and turned them to fire. Never before had I seen the mountain-land so clear, for far back into the east and west I saw mountain tops set as close as flowers in a border, black crags seamed with silver lines which I knew for mighty waterfalls, and below at my feet the lower slopes fresh with the dewy green of spring. A name stuck in my memory from the last night's talk.

"Where are the Scarts of the Muneraw?" I asked.

The shepherd pointed to the great hill which bears the name, and which lies, a huge mass, above the watershed.

"D'ye see yon corrie at the east that runs straucht up the side? It looks a bit scart, but it's sae deep that it's aye derk at the bottom o't. Weel, at the tap o' the rig it meets anither corrie that runs doun the ither side, and that one they ca' the Scarts. There is a sort o' burn in it that flows intil the Dule and sae intil the Aller, and, indeed, if ye were gaun there it wad be from Aller Glen that your best road wad lie. But it's an ill bit, and ye'll be sair guidit if ye try't."

There he left me and went across the glen, while I struck upwards over the ridge. At the top I halted and looked down on the wide glen of the Caulds, which there is little better than a bog, but lower down grows into a green pastoral valley. The great Muneraw still dominated the landscape, and the black scaur on its side seemed blacker than before. The place fascinated me, for in that fresh morning air the shepherd's fears seemed monstrous. " Some day," said I to myself, " I will go and explore the whole of that mighty hill." Then I descended and struggled over the moss, found the Nick, and in two hours' time was on the loch's edge.

I have little in the way of good to report of the fishing. For perhaps one hour the trout took well ; after that they sulked steadily for the day. The promise, too, of fine weather had been deceptive. By midday the rain was falling in that soft soaking fashion which gives no hope of clearing. The mist was down to the edge of the water, and I cast my flies into a blind sea of white. It was hopeless work, and yet from a sort of ill-temper I stuck to it long after my better judgment had warned me of its folly. At last, about three in the afternoon, I struck my camp, and prepared myself for a long and toilsome retreat.

And long and toilsome it was beyond anything I had ever encountered. Had I had a vestige of sense I would have followed the burn from the loch down to the Forest House. The place was shut up, but the keeper would gladly have given me shelter for the night. But foolish pride was too strong in me. I had found my road in mist before, and could do it again.

Before I got to the top of the hill I had repented

my decision ; when I got there I repented it more.
For below me was a dizzy chaos of grey ; there was
no landmark visible ; and before me I knew was
the bog through which the Caulds Water twined.
I had crossed it with some trouble in the morning,
but then I had light to pick my steps. Now I could
only stumble on, and in five minutes I might be in
a bog hole, and in five more in a better world.

But there was no help to be got from hesitation,
so with a rueful courage I set off. The place was
if possible worse than I had feared. Wading up
to the knees with nothing before you but a blank
wall of mist and the cheerful consciousness that
your next step may be your last—such was my
state for one weary mile. The stream itself was
high, and rose to my armpits, and once and again
I only saved myself by a violent leap backwards
from a pitiless green slough. But at last it was
past, and I was once more on the solid ground of
the hillside.

Now, in the thick weather I had crossed the
glen much lower down than in the morning, and
the result was that the hill on which I stood was
one of the giants which, with the Muneraw for
centre, guard the watershed. Had I taken the
proper way, the Nick o' the Threshes would have
led me to the Caulds, and then once over the bog
a little ridge was all that stood between me and
the glen of Farawa. But instead I had come a
wild cross-country road, and was now, though I
did not know it, nearly as far from my destination
as at the start.

Well for me that I did not know, for I was wet and dispirited, and had I not fancied myself all but home, I should scarcely have had the energy to make this last ascent. But soon I found it was not the little ridge I had expected. I looked at my watch and saw that it was five o'clock. When, after the weariest climb, I lay on a piece of level ground which seemed the top, I was not surprised to find that it was now seven. The darkening must be at hand, and sure enough the mist seemed to be deepening into a greyish black. I began to grow desperate. Here was I on the summit of some infernal mountain, without any certainty where my road lay. I was lost with a vengeance, and at the thought I began to be acutely afraid.

I took what seemed to me the way I had come, and began to descend steeply. Then something made me halt, and the next instant I was lying on my face trying painfully to retrace my steps. For I had found myself slipping, and before I could stop, my feet were dangling over a precipice with Heaven alone knows how many yards of sheer mist between me and the bottom. Then I tried keeping the ridge, and took that to the right, which I thought would bring me nearer home. It was no good trying to think out a direction, for in the fog my brain was running round, and I seemed to stand on a pin-point of space where the laws of the compass had ceased to hold.

It was the roughest sort of walking, now stepping warily over acres of loose stones, now crawling down the face of some battered rock, and now

wading in the long dripping heather. The soft
rain had begun to fall again, which completed my
discomfort. I was now seriously tired, and, like
all men who in their day have bent too much over
books, I began to feel it in my back. My spine
ached, and my breath came in short broken pants.
It was a pitiable state of affairs for an honest man
who had never encountered much grave discomfort.
To ease myself I was compelled to leave my basket
behind me, trusting to return and find it, if I
should ever reach safety and discover on what
pathless hill I had been strayed. My rod I used
as a staff, but it was of little use, for my fingers
were getting too numb to hold it.

Suddenly from the blankness I heard a sound
as of human speech. At first I thought it mere
craziness—the cry of a weasel or a hill bird dis-
torted by my ears. But again it came, thick and
faint, as through acres of mist, and yet clearly the
sound of "articulate-speaking men." In a moment I lost my despair and cried out in answer.
This was some forwandered traveller like myself,
and between us we could surely find some road
to safety. So I yelled back at the pitch of my
voice and waited intently.

But the sound ceased, and there was utter silence
again. Still I waited, and then from some place
much nearer came the same soft mumbling speech.
I could make nothing of it. Heard in that drear
place it made the nerves tense and the heart
timorous. It was the strangest jumble of vowels
and consonants I had ever met.

A dozen solutions flashed through my brain. It was some maniac talking Jabberwock to himself. It was some belated traveller whose wits had given out in fear. Perhaps it was only some shepherd who was amusing himself thus, and whiling the way with nonsense. Once again I cried out and waited.

Then suddenly in the hollow trough of mist before me, where things could still be half discerned, there appeared a figure. It was little and squat and dark ; naked, apparently, but so rough with hair that it wore the appearance of a skin-covered being. It crossed my line of vision, not staying for a moment, but in its face and eyes there seemed to lurk an elder world of mystery and barbarism, a troll-like life which was too horrible for words.

The shepherd's fear came back on me like a thunderclap. For one awful instant my legs failed me, and I had almost fallen. The next I had turned and ran shrieking up the hill.

If he who may read this narrative has never felt the force of an overmastering terror, then let him thank his Maker and pray that he never may. I am no weak child, but a strong grown man, accredited in general with sound sense and little suspected of hysterics. And yet I went up that brae face with my heart fluttering like a bird and my throat aching with fear. I screamed in short dry gasps ; involuntarily, for my mind was beyond any purpose. I felt that beast-like clutch at my throat ; those red eyes seemed to be staring at me

from the mist ; I heard ever behind and before and
on all sides the patter of those inhuman feet.

Before I knew I was down, slipping over a rock
and falling some dozen feet into a soft marshy
hollow. I was conscious of lying still for a second
and whimpering like a child. But as I lay there
I awoke to the silence of the place. There was
no sound of pursuit ; perhaps they had lost my
track and given up. My courage began to return,
and from this it was an easy step to hope. Perhaps after all it had been merely an illusion, for
folk do not see clearly in the mist, and I was already done with weariness.

But even as I lay in the green moss and began
to hope, the faces of my pursuers grew up through
the mist. I stumbled madly to my feet ; but I
was hemmed in, the rock behind and my enemies
before. With a cry I rushed forward, and struck
wildly with my rod at the first dark body. It was
as if I had struck an animal, and the next second
the thing was wrenched from my grasp. But still
they came no nearer. I stood trembling there in
the centre of those malignant devils, my brain a
mere weathercock, and my heart crushed shapeless
with horror. At last the end came, for with the
vigour of madness I flung myself on the nearest,
and we rolled on the ground. Then the monstrous things seemed to close over me, and with
a choking cry I passed into unconsciousness.

CHAPTER IV

THE DARKNESS THAT IS UNDER THE EARTH

THERE is an unconsciousness that is not wholly dead, where a man feels numbly and the body lives without the brain. I was beyond speech or thought, and yet I felt the upward or downward motion as the way lay in hill or glen, and I most assuredly knew when the open air was changed for the close underground. I could feel dimly that lights were flared in my face, and that I was laid in some bed on the earth. Then with the stopping of movement the real sleep of weakness seized me, and for long I knew nothing of this mad world.

*　　*　　*　　*　　*　　*

Morning came over the moors with bird song and the glory of fine weather. The streams were still rolling in spate, but the hill pastures were alight with dawn, and the little seams of snow were glistening like white fire. A ray from the sunrise cleft its path somehow into the abyss, and danced on the wall above my couch. It caught my eye as I wakened, and for long I lay crazily wondering what it meant. My head was splitting

with pain, and in my heart was the same fluttering
nameless fear. I did not wake to full consciousness ; not till the twinkle of sun from the clean
bright out-of-doors caught my face did I realize
that I lay in a great dark place with a glow of
dull firelight in the middle.

In time things rose and moved around me,
a few ragged shapes of men, without clothing,
shambling with their huge feet and looking towards
me with curved beast-like glances. I tried to
marshal my thoughts, and slowly, bit by bit, I
built up the present. There was no question
to my mind of dreaming ; the past hours had
scored reality upon my brain. Yet I cannot
say that fear was my chief feeling. The first
crazy terror had subsided, and now I felt mainly
a sickened disgust with just a tinge of curiosity.
I found that my knife, watch, flask, and money
had gone, but they had left me a map of the countryside. It seemed strange to look at the calico,
with the name of a London printer stamped on
the back, and lines of railway and highroad running through every shire. Decent and comfortable civilization ! And here was I a prisoner in
this den of nameless folk, and in the midst of a
life which history knew not.

Courage is a virtue which grows with reflection
and the absence of the immediate peril. I thought
myself into some sort of resolution, and lo ! when
the Folk approached me and bound my feet I
was back at once in the most miserable terror.
They tied me, all but my hands, with some strong

cord, and carried me to the centre, where the fire
was glowing. Their soft touch was the acutest
torture to my nerves, but I stifled my cries lest
some one should lay his hand on my mouth. Had
that happened, I am convinced my reason would
have failed me.

So there I lay in the shine of the fire, with the
circle of unknown things around me. There
seemed but three or four, but I took no note of
number. They talked huskily among themselves
in a tongue which sounded all gutturals. Slowly
my fear became less an emotion than a habit,
and I had room for the smallest shade of curiosity.
I strained my ear to catch a word, but it was a
mere chaos of sound. The thing ran and thun-
dered in my brain as I stared dumbly into the
vacant air. Then I thought that unless I spoke
I should certainly go crazy, for my head was beginning to swim at the strange cooing noise.

I spoke a word or two in my best Gaelic, and
they closed round me inquiringly. Then I was
sorry I had spoken, for my words had brought
them nearer, and I shrank at the thought. But
as the faint echoes of my speech hummed in the
rock chamber, I was struck by a curious kinship
of sound. Mine was sharper, more distinct, and
staccato ; theirs was blurred, formless, but still
with a certain root resemblance.

Then from the back there came an older being,
who seemed to have heard my words. He was
like some foul grey badger, his red eyes sightless,
and his hands trembling on a stump of bog oak.

The others made way for him with such deference
as they were capable of, and the thing squatted
down by me and spoke.

To my amazement his words were familiar.
It was some manner of speech akin to the Gaelic,
but broadened, lengthened, coarsened. I remembered an old book tongue, commonly supposed
to be an impure dialect once used in Brittany,
which I had met in the course of my researches. The words recalled it, and as far as
I could remember the thing, I asked him who he
was and where the place might be.

He answered me in the same speech—still
more broadened, lengthened, coarsened. I lay
back with sheer amazement. I had found the
key to this unearthly life.

For a little an insatiable curiosity, the ardour
of the scholar, prevailed. I forgot the horror
of the place, and thought only of the fact that
here before me was the greatest find that scholarship had ever made. I was precipitated into the
heart of the past. Here must be the fountain-
head of all legends, the chrysalis of all beliefs.
I actually grew light-hearted. This strange folk
around me were now no more shapeless things
of terror, but objects of research and experiment.
I almost came to think them not unfriendly.

For an hour I enjoyed the highest of earthly
pleasures. In that strange conversation I heard
—in fragments and suggestions—the history of
the craziest survival the world has ever seen.
I heard of the struggles with invaders, preserved

as it were in a sort of shapeless poetry. There
were bitter words against the Gaelic oppressor,
bitterer words against the Saxon stranger, and
for a moment ancient hatreds flared into life.
Then there came the tale of the hill refuge, the
morbid hideous existence preserved for centuries
amid a changing world. I heard fragments of
old religions, primeval names of god and goddess,
half-understood by the Folk, but to me the key
to a hundred puzzles. Tales which survive to
us in broken disjointed riddles were intact here
in living form. I lay on my elbow and questioned feverishly. At any moment they might
become morose and refuse to speak. Clearly
it was my duty to make the most of a brief good
fortune.

And then the tale they told me grew more
hideous. I heard of the circumstances of the
life itself and their daily shifts for existence. It
was a murderous chronicle—a history of lust
and rapine and unmentionable deeds in the darkness. One thing they had early recognized—
that the race could not be maintained within
itself; so that ghoulish carrying away of little
girls from the lowlands began, which I had heard
of but never credited. Shut up in those dismal
holes, the girls soon died, and when the new race
had grown up the plunder had been repeated.
Then there were bestial murders in lonely cot-
tages, done for God knows what purpose. Sometimes the occupant had seen more than was safe,
sometimes the deed was the mere exuberance of

a lust of slaying. As they gabbled their tales my heart's blood froze, and I lay back in the agonies of fear. If they had used the others thus, what way of escape was open for myself? I had been brought to this place, and not murdered on the spot. Clearly there was torture before death in store for me, and I confess I quailed at the thought.

But none molested me. The elders continued to jabber out their stories, while I lay tense and deaf. Then to my amazement food was brought and placed beside me — almost with respect. Clearly my murder was not a thing of the immediate future. The meal was some form of mutton—perhaps the shepherd's lost ewes—and a little smoking was all the cooking it had got. I strove to eat, but the tasteless morsels choked me. Then they set drink before me in a curious cup, which I seized on eagerly, for my mouth was dry with thirst. The vessel was of gold, rudely formed, but of the pure metal, and a coarse design in circles ran round the middle. This was surprising enough, but a greater wonder awaited me. The liquor was not water, as I had guessed, but a sort of sweet ale, a miracle of flavour. The taste was curious, but somehow familiar; it was like no wine I had ever drunk, and yet I had known that flavour all my life. I sniffed at the brim, and there rose a faint fragrance of thyme and heather honey and the sweet things of the moorland. I almost dropped it in my surprise; for here in this rude place I had stumbled upon that lost delicacy of the North, the heather ale.

For a second I was entranced with my discovery, and then the wonder of the cup claimed my attention. Was it a mere relic of pillage, or had this folk some hidden mine of the precious metal? Gold had once been common in these hills. There were the traces of mines on Cairnsmore; shepherds had found it in the gravel of the Gled Water; and the name of a house at the head of the Clachlands meant the "Home of Gold."

Once more I began my questions, and they answered them willingly. There and then I heard that secret for which many had died in old time, the secret of the heather ale. They told of the gold in the hills, of corries where the sand gleamed and abysses where the rocks were veined. All this they told me, freely, without a scruple. And then, like a clap, came the awful thought that this, too, spelled death. These were secrets which this race aforetime had guarded with their lives; they told them generously to me because there was no fear of betrayal. I should go no more out from this place.

The thought put me into a new sweat of terror —not of death, mind you, but of the unknown horrors which might precede the final suffering. I lay silent, and after binding my hands they began to leave me and go off to other parts of the cave. I dozed in the horrible half-swoon of fear, conscious only of my shaking limbs, and

the great dull glow of the fire in the centre. Then
I became calmer. After all, they had treated
me with tolerable kindness ; I had spoken their
language, which few of their victims could have
done for many a century ; it might be that I
had found favour in their eyes. For a little I
comforted myself with this delusion, till I caught
sight of a wooden box in a corner. It was of
modern make, one such as grocers use to pack
provisions in. It had some address nailed on it,
and an aimless curiosity compelled me to creep
thither and read it. A torn and weather-stained
scrap of paper, with the nails at the corner rusty
with age ; but something of the address might
still be made out. Amid the stains my feverish
eyes read, " To Mr. M——, Carrickfey, by Allerfoot Station."

The ruined cottage in the hollow of the waste
with the single gnarled apple tree was before
me in a twinkling. I remembered the shepherd's
shrinking from the place and the name, and his
wild eyes when he told me of the thing that had
happened there. I seemed to see the old man in
his moorland cottage, thinking no evil ; the sudden entry of the nameless things ; and then the
eyes glazed in unspeakable terror. I felt my lips
dry and burning. Above me was the vault of
rock ; in the distance I saw the fire-glow and the
shadows of shapes moving around it. My fright
was too great for inaction, so I crept from the
couch, and silently, stealthily, with tottering
steps and bursting heart, I began to reconnoitre.

But I was still bound, my arms tightly, my legs more loosely, but yet firm enough to hinder flight. I could not get my hands at my leg straps, still less could I undo the manacles. I rolled on the floor, seeking some sharp edge of rock, but all had been worn smooth by the use of centuries. Then suddenly an idea came upon me like an inspiration. The sounds from the fire seemed to have ceased, and I could hear them repeated from another and more distant part of the cave. The Folk had left their orgy round the blaze, and at the end of the long tunnel I saw its glow fall unimpeded upon the floor. Once there, I might burn off my fetters and be free to turn my thoughts to escape.

I crawled a little way with much labour. Then suddenly I came abreast an opening in the wall, through which a path went. It was a long straight rock-cutting, and at the end I saw a gleam of pale light. It must be the open air; the way of escape was prepared for me; and with a prayer I made what speed I could towards the fire.

I rolled on the verge, but the fuel was peat, and the warm ashes would not burn the cords. In desperation I went farther, and my clothes began to singe, while my face ached beyond endurance. But yet I got no nearer my object. The strips of hide warped and cracked, but did not burn. Then in a last effort I thrust my wrists bodily into the glow and held them there. In an instant I drew them out with a groan of pain, scarred and sore, but to my joy with the band

snapped in one place. Weak as I was, it was
now easy to free myself, and then came the untying
of my legs. My hands trembled, my eyes were
dazed with hurry, and I was longer over the job
than need have been. But at length I had loosed
my cramped knees and stood on my feet, a free
man once more.

I kicked off my boots, and fled noiselessly down
the passage to the tunnel mouth. Apparently
it was close on evening, for the white light had
faded to a pale yellow. But it was daylight, and
that was all I sought, and I ran for it as eagerly
as ever runner ran to a goal. I came out on a
rock shelf, beneath which a moraine of boulders
fell away in a chasm to a dark loch. It was all
but night, but I could see the gnarled and for-
tressed rocks rise in ramparts above, and below
the unknown screes and cliffs which make the
side of the Muneraw a place only for foxes and
the fowls of the air.

The first taste of liberty is an intoxication,
and assuredly I was mad when I leaped down
among the boulders. Happily at the top of the
gully the stones were large and stable, else the
noise would certainly have discovered me. Down
I went, slipping, praying, my charred wrists
aching, and my stockinged feet wet with blood.
Soon I was in the jaws of the cleft, and a pale
star rose before me. I have always been timid
in the face of great rocks, and now, had not an
awful terror been dogging my footsteps, no power
on earth could have driven me to that descent.

Soon I left the boulders behind, and came to long
spouts of little stones, which moved with me till
the hillside seemed sinking under my feet. Sometimes I was face downwards, once and again I
must have fallen for yards. Had there been a
cliff at the foot, I should have gone over it without
resistance; but by the providence of God the
spout ended in a long curve into the heather of
the bog.

When I found my feet once more on soft boggy
earth, my strength was renewed within me. A
hope of escape sprang up in my heart. For a
second I looked back. There was a great line
of shingle with the cliffs beyond, and above all
the unknown blackness of the cleft. There lay
my terror, and I set off running across the bog for
dear life. My mind was clear enough to know
my road. If I held round the loch in front I
should come to a burn which fed the Farawa
stream, on whose banks stood the shepherd's
cottage. The loch could not be far; once at the
Farawa I would have the light of the shieling
clear before me.

Suddenly I heard behind me, as if coming from
the hillside, the patter of feet. It was the sound
which white hares make in the winter-time on
a noiseless frosty day as they patter over the
snow. I have heard the same soft noise from a
herd of deer when they changed their pastures.
Strange that so kindly a sound should put the very
fear of death in my heart. I ran madly, blindly,
yet thinking shrewdly. The loch was before me.

Somewhere I had read or heard, I do not know
where, that the brutish aboriginal races of the
North could not swim. I myself swam power-
fully ; could I but cross the loch I should save
two miles of a desperate country.

There was no time to lose, for the patter was
coming nearer, and I was almost at the loch's
edge. I tore off my coat and rushed in. The
bottom was mossy, and I had to struggle far
before I found any depth. Something plashed in
the water before me, and then something else a
little behind. The thought that I was a mark for
unknown missiles made me crazy with fright, and
I struck fiercely out for the other shore. A gleam
of moonlight was on the water at the burn's exit,
and thither I guided myself. I found the thing
difficult enough in itself, for my hands ached, and
I was numb from my bonds. But my fancy raised
a thousand phantoms to vex me. Swimming in
that black bog water, pursued by those nameless
things, I seemed to be in a world of horror far
removed from the kindly world of men. My
strength seemed inexhaustible from my terror.
Monsters at the bottom of the water seemed to
bite at my feet, and the pain of my wrists made
me believe that the loch was boiling hot, and that
I was in some hellish place of torment.

I came out on a spit of gravel above the burn
mouth, and set off down the ravine of the burn.
It was a strait place, strewn with rocks ; but now
and then the hill turf came in stretches, and eased
my wounded feet. Soon the fall became more

CHAPTER V

THE TROUBLES OF A CONSCIENCE

MY body and senses slept, for I was utterly tired, but my brain all the night was on fire with horrid fancies. Again I was in that accursed cave; I was torturing my hands in the fire; I was slipping barefoot among jagged boulders; and then with bursting heart I was toiling the last mile with the cottage light—now grown to a great fire in the heavens—blazing before me.

It was broad daylight when I awoke, and I thanked God for the comfortable rays of the sun. I had been laid in a box-bed off the inner room, and my first sight was the shepherd sitting with folded arms in a chair regarding me solemnly. I rose and began to dress, feeling my legs and arms still tremble with weariness. The shepherd's sister bound up my scarred wrists and put an ointment on my burns; and, limping like an old man, I went into the kitchen.

I could eat little breakfast, for my throat seemed dry and narrow; but they gave me some whisky-and-milk, which put strength into my body. All the time the brother and sister sat in silence, regarding me with covert glances.

"Ye have been delivered from the jaws o' the Pit," said the man at length. "See that," and he held out to me a thin shaft of flint. "I fand that in the door this morning."

I took it, let it drop, and stared vacantly at the window. My nerves had been too much tried to be roused by any new terror. Out of doors it was fair weather, flying gleams of April sunlight and the soft colours of spring. I felt dazed, isolated, cut off from my easy past and pleasing future, a companion of horrors and the sport of nameless things. Then suddenly my eye fell on my books heaped on the table, and the old distant civilization seemed for the moment inexpressibly dear.

"I must go—at once. And you must come too. You cannot stay here. I tell you it is death. If you knew what I know you would be crying out with fear. How far is it to Allermuir? Eight, fifteen miles; and then ten down Glen Aller to Allerfoot, and then the railway. We must go together while it is daylight, and perhaps we may be untouched. But quick, there is not a moment to lose." And I was on my shaky feet, and bustling among my possessions.

"I'll gang wi' ye to the station," said the shepherd, "for ye're clearly no fit to look after yourself. My sister will bide and keep the house. If naething has touched us this ten year, naething will touch us the day."

"But you cannot stay. You are mad," I began;
but he cut me short with the words, "I trust in
God."

"In any case let your sister come with us. I
dare not think of a woman alone in this place."

"I'll bide," said she. "I'm no feared as lang
as I'm indoors and there's steeks on the windies."

So I packed my few belongings as best I could,
flung my books into a haversack, and, gripping
the shepherd's arm nervously, crossed the threshold. The glen was full of sunlight. There lay
the long shining links of the Farawa burn, the
rough hills tumbled beyond, and far over all the
scarred and distant forehead of the Muneraw. I
had always looked on moorland country as the
freshest on earth—clean, wholesome, and homely.
But now the uplands seemed like a horrible pit.
When I looked to the hills my breath choked in
my throat, and the feel of soft heather below my
feet set my heart trembling.

It was a slow journey to the inn at Allermuir.
For one thing, no power on earth would draw me
within sight of the shieling of Carrickfey, so we
had to cross a shoulder of hill and make our way
down a difficult glen, and then over a treacherous
moss. The lochs were now gleaming like fretted
silver; but to me, in my dreadful knowledge, they
seemed more eerie than on that grey day when I
came. At last my eyes were cheered by the sight
of a meadow and a fence; then we were on a little
byroad; and soon the fir-woods and corn-lands of
Allercleuch were plain before us.

The shepherd came no farther, but with brief
good-bye turned his solemn face hillwards. I hired
a trap and a man to drive, and down the ten miles
of Glen Aller I struggled to keep my thoughts
from the past. I thought of the kindly South
Country, of Oxford, of anything comfortable and
civilized. My driver pointed out the objects of
interest as in duty bound, but his words fell on
unheeding ears. At last he said something which
roused me indeed to interest—the interest of the
man who hears the word he fears most in the
world. On the left side of the river there suddenly
sprang into view a long gloomy cleft in the hills,
with a vista of dark mountains behind, down
which a stream of considerable size poured its
waters.

" That is the Water o' Dule," said the man in
a reverent voice. " A graund water to fish, but
dangerous to life, for it's a' linns. Awa at the
heid they say there's a terrible wild place called
the Scarts o' Muneraw,—that's a shouther o' the
muckle hill itsel' that ye see,—but I've never been
there, and I never kent ony man that had either."

At the station, which is a mile from the village
of Allerfoot, I found I had some hours to wait on
my train for the south. I dared not trust myself
for one moment alone, so I hung about the goods
shed, talked vacantly to the porters, and when
one went to the village for tea I accompanied him,
and to his wonder entertained him at the inn.
When I returned I found on the platform a stray
bagman who was that evening going to London.

without more words I left him, hot, angry with myself, and tantalized by the unattainable.

I might relate my *bona-fide* experience, but would men believe me? I must bring proofs, I must complete my researches, so as to make them incapable of disbelief. And there in those deserts was waiting the key. There lay the greatest discovery of the century—nay, of the millennium. There, too, lay the road to wealth such as I had never dreamed of. Could I succeed, I should be famous for ever. I would revolutionize history and anthropology; I would systematize folklore; I would show the world of men the pit whence they were digged and the rock whence they were hewn.

And then began a game of battledore between myself and my conscience.

"You are a coward," said my conscience.

"I am sufficiently brave," I would answer. "I have seen things and yet lived. The terror is more than mortal, and I cannot face it."

"You are a coward," said my conscience.

"I am not bound to go there again. It would be purely for my own aggrandizement if I went, and not for any matter of duty."

"Nevertheless you are a coward," said my conscience.

"In any case the matter can wait."

"You are a coward."

* * * * * *

Then came one awful midsummer night, when I lay sleepless and fought the thing out with myself. I knew that the strife was hopeless, that I should have no peace in this world again unless I made the attempt. The dawn was breaking when I came to the final resolution ; and when I rose and looked at my face in a mirror, lo ! it was white and lined and drawn like a man of sixty.

CHAPTER VI

SUMMER ON THE MOORS

THE next morning I packed a bag with some changes of clothing and a collection of note-books, and went up to town. The first thing I did was to pay a visit to my solicitors. "I am about to travel," said I, "and I wish to have all things settled in case any accident should happen to me." So I arranged for the disposal of my property in case of death, and added a codicil which puzzled the lawyers. If I did not return within six months, communications were to be entered into with the shepherd at the shiel-ing of Farawa—post-town Allerfoot. If he could produce any papers, they were to be put into the hands of certain friends, published, and the cost charged to my estate. From my solicitors I went to a gunmaker's in Regent Street and bought an ordinary six-chambered revolver, feel-ing much as a man must feel who proposed to cross the Atlantic in a skiff and purchased a small lifebelt as a precaution.

I took the night express to the North, and, for a marvel, I slept. When I awoke about four

63

we were on the verge of Westmoreland, and stony
hills blocked the horizon. At first I hailed the
mountain-land gladly; sleep for the moment
had caused forgetfulness of my terrors. But
soon a turn of the line brought me in full view of
a heathery moor, running far to a confusion of
distant peaks. I remembered my mission and
my fate, and if ever condemned criminal felt
a more bitter regret I pity his case. Why should
I alone among the millions of this happy isle be
singled out as the repository of a ghastly secret,
and be cursed by a conscience which would not
let it rest?

I came to Allerfoot early in the forenoon,
and got a trap to drive me up the valley. It
was a lowering grey day, hot and yet sunless.
A sort of heat haze cloaked the hills, and every
now and then a smurr of rain would meet us on
the road, and in a minute be over. I felt wretchedly dispirited; and when at last the whitewashed kirk of Allermuir came into sight and the
broken-backed bridge of Aller, man's eyes seemed
to have looked on no drearier scene since time
began.

I ate what meal I could get, for, fears or no,
I was voraciously hungry. Then I asked the
landlord to find me some man who would show
me the road to Farawa. I demanded company,
not for protection—for what could two men do
against such brutish strength?—but to keep my
mind from its own thoughts.

The man looked at me anxiously.

" Are ye acquaint wi' the folks, then ? " he asked.

I said I was, that I had often stayed in the cottage.

" Ye ken that they've a name for being queer. The man never comes here forbye once or twice a year, and he has few dealings wi' other herds. He's got an ill name, too, for losing sheep. I dinna like the country ava. Up by yon Mune-raw—no that I've ever been there, but I've seen it afar off—is enough to put a man daft for the rest o' his days. What's taking ye thereaways ? It's no the time for the fishing ? "

I told him that I was a botanist going to explore certain hill crevices for rare ferns. He shook his head, and then after some delay found me an ostler who would accompany me to the cottage.

The man was a shock-headed, long-limbed fellow, with fierce red hair and a humorous eye. He talked sociably about his life, answered my hasty questions with deftness, and beguiled me for the moment out of myself. I passed the melancholy lochs, and came in sight of the great stony hills without the trepidation I had expected. Here at my side was one who found some humour even in those uplands. But one thing I noted which brought back the old uneasiness. He took the road which led us farthest from Carrickfey, and when to try him I proposed the other, he vetoed it with emphasis.

After this his good spirits departed, and he grew distrustful.

"What maks ye a freend o' the herd at Far-awa?" he demanded a dozen times.

Finally, I asked him if he knew the man, and had seen him lately.

"I dinna ken him, and I hadna seen him for years till a fortnicht syne, when a' Allermuir saw him. He cam doun one afternoon to the public-hoose, and begood to drink. He had aye been kenned for a terrible godly kind o' a man, so ye may believe folk wondered at this. But when he had stuck to the drink for twae days, and filled himsel' blind-fou half a dozen o' times, he took a fit o' repentance, and raved and blethered about siccan a life as he led in the muirs. There was some said he was speakin' serious, but maist thocht it was juist daftness."

"And what did he speak about?" I asked sharply.

"I canna verra weel tell ye. It was about some kind o' bogle that lived in the Muneraw— that's the shouthers o't ye see yonder—and it seems that the bogle killed his sheep and frichted himsel'. He was aye betherin', too, about something or somebody ca'd Grave; but oh! the man wasna wise." And my companion shook a contemptuous head.

And then below us in the valley we saw the shieling, with a thin shaft of smoke rising into the rainy grey weather. The man left me, sturdily refusing any fee. "I wantit my legs stretched as weel as you. A walk in the hills is neither here nor there to a stoot man. When will ye be back, sir?"

The question was well-timed. "To-morrow fortnight," I said, "and I want somebody from Allermuir to come out here in the morning and carry some baggage. Will you see to that?"

He said "Ay," and went off, while I scrambled down the hill to the cottage. Nervousness possessed me, and though it was broad daylight and the whole place lay plain before me, I ran pell-mell, and did not stop till I reached the door.

The place was utterly empty. Unmade beds, unwashed dishes, a hearth strewn with the ashes of peat, and dust thick on everything, proclaimed the absence of inmates. I began to be hideously frightened. Had the shepherd, and his sister also, disappeared? Was I left alone, with a dozen lonely miles between me and human dwellings? I could not return alone; better this horrible place than the unknown perils of the out-of-doors. Hastily I barricaded the door, and to the best of my power shuttered the windows; and then with dreary forebodings I sat down to wait on fortune.

In a little I heard a long swinging step outside and the sound of dogs. Joyfully I opened the latch, and there was the shepherd's grim face waiting stolidly on what might appear.

At the sight of me he stepped back. "What in the Lord's name are ye daein' here?" he asked. "Didna ye get eneuch afore?"

"Come in," I said sharply. "I want to talk."

In he came with those blessed dogs—what a comfort it was to look on their great honest faces! He sat down on the untidy bed and waited.

"I came because I could not stay away. I saw too much to give me any peace elsewhere. I must go back, even though I risk my life for it. The cause of scholarship demands it as well as the cause of humanity."

"Is that a' the news ye hae ?" he said. "Weel, I've mair to tell ye. Three weeks syne my sister Margit was lost, and I've never seen her mair."

My jaw fell, and I could only stare at him.

"I cam hame from the hill at nightfa' and she was gone. I lookit for her up hill and doun, but I couldna find her. Syne I think I went daft. I went to the Scarts and huntit them up and doun, but no sign could I see. The Folk can bide quiet enough when they want. Syne I went to Allermuir and drank mysel' blind— me, that's a God-fearing man and a saved soul; but the Lord help me, I didna ken what I was at. That's my news, and day and night I wander thae hills, seekin' for what I canna find."

"But, man, are you mad ?" I cried. "Surely there are neighbours to help you. There is a law in the land, and you had only to find the nearest police-office and compel them to assist you."

"What guid can man dae ?" he asked. "An army o' sodgers couldna find that hidy-hole. Forby, when I went into Allermuir wi' my story the folk thocht me daft. It was that set me drinking, for—the Lord forgive me !—I wasna my ain maister. I threepit till I was hairse, but the bodies just lauch'd." And he lay back on the bed like a man mortally tired.

Grim though the tidings were, I can only say that my chief feeling was of comfort. Pity for the new tragedy had swallowed up my fear. I had now a purpose, and a purpose, too, not of curiosity but of mercy.

"I go to-morrow morning to the Muneraw. But first I want to give you something to do." And I drew roughly a chart of the place on the back of a letter. "Go into Allermuir to-morrow, and give this paper to the landlord at the inn. The letter will tell him what to do. He is to raise at once all the men he can get, and come to the place on the chart marked with a cross. Tell him life depends on his hurry."

The shepherd nodded. "D'ye ken the Folk are watching for you? They let me pass without trouble, for they've nae use for me, but I see fine they're seeking you. Ye'll no gang half a mile the morn afore they grip ye."

"So much the better," I said. "That will take me quicker to the place I want to be at."

"And I'm to gang to Allermuir the morn," he repeated, with the air of a child conning a lesson. "But what if they'll no believe me?"

"They'll believe the letter."

"Maybe," he said, and relapsed into a doze.

I set myself to put that house in order, to rouse the fire, and prepare some food. It was dismal work; and meantime outside the night darkened and a great wind rose, which howled round the walls and lashed the rain on the windows.

CHAPTER VII

"IN TUAS MANUS, DOMINE!"

I HAD not gone twenty yards from the cottage door ere I knew I was watched. I had left the shepherd still dozing, in the half-conscious state of a dazed and broken man. All night the wind had wakened me at intervals, and now in the half-light of morn the weather seemed more vicious than ever. The wind cut my ears, the whole firmament was full of the rendings and thunders of the storm. Rain fell in blinding sheets, the heath was a marsh, and it was the most I could do to struggle against the hurricane which stopped my breath. And all the while I knew I was not alone in the desert.

All men know—in imagination or in experience—the sensation of being spied on. The nerves tingle, the skin grows hot and prickly, and there is a queer sinking of the heart. Intensify this common feeling a hundredfold, and you get a tenth part of what I suffered. I am telling a plain tale, and record bare physical facts. My lips stood out from my teeth as I heard, or felt, a rustle in the heather, a scraping among

70

stones. Some subtle magnetic link seemed established between my body and the mysterious world around. I became sick—acutely sick—with the ceaseless apprehension.

My fright became so complete that when I turned a corner of rock, or stepped in deep heather, I seemed to feel a body rub against mine. This continued all the way up the Farawa water, and then up its feeder to the little lonely loch. It kept me from looking forward; but it likewise kept me in such a sweat of fright that I was ready to faint. Then the notion came upon me to test this fancy of mine. If I was tracked thus closely, clearly the trackers would bar my way if I turned back. So I wheeled round and walked a dozen paces down the glen.

Nothing stopped me. I was about to turn again, when something made me take six more paces. At the fourth something rustled in the heather, and my neck was gripped as in a vice. I had already made up my mind on what I would do. I would be perfectly still, I would conquer my fear, and let them do as they pleased with me so long as they took me to their dwelling. But at the touch of the hands my resolutions fled. I struggled and screamed. Then something was clapped on my mouth, speech and strength went from me, and once more I was back in the maudlin childhood of terror.

*   *   *   *   *   *

In the cave it was always a dusky twilight. I seemed to be lying in the same place, with the same dull glare of firelight far off, and the same close stupefying smell. One of the creatures was standing silently at my side, and I asked him some trivial question. He turned and shambled down the passage, leaving me alone.

Then he returned with another, and they talked their guttural talk to me. I scarcely listened till I remembered that in a sense I was here of my own accord, and on a definite mission. The purport of their speech seemed to be that, now I had returned, I must beware of a second flight. Once I had been spared; a second time I should be killed without mercy.

I assented gladly. The Folk, then, had some use for me. I felt my errand prospering.

Then the old creature which I had seen before crept out of some corner and squatted beside me. He put a claw on my shoulder, a horrible, corrugated, skeleton thing, hairy to the finger-tips and nailless. He grinned, too, with toothless gums, and his hideous old voice was like a file on sandstone.

I asked questions, but he would only grin and jabber, looking now and then furtively over his shoulder towards the fire.

I coaxed and humoured him, till he launched into a narrative of which I could make nothing. It seemed a mere string of names, with certain words repeated at fixed intervals. Then it flashed on me that this might be a religious incantation. I had discovered remnants of a ritual and a mythology among them. It was possible that these were sacred days, and that I had stumbled upon some rude celebration.

I caught a word or two and repeated them. He looked at me curiously. Then I asked him some leading question, and he replied with clearness. My guess was right. The midsummer week was the holy season of the year, when sacrifices were offered to the gods.

The notion of sacrifices disquieted me, and I would fain have asked further. But the creature would speak no more. He hobbled off, and left me alone in the rock chamber to listen to a strange sound which hung ceaselessly about me. It must be the storm without, like a park of artillery rattling among the crags. A storm of storms surely, for the place echoed and hummed, and to my unquiet eye the very rock of the roof seemed to shake.

Apparently my existence was forgotten, for I lay long before any one returned. Then it was merely one who brought food, the same strange meal as before, and left hastily. When I had eaten I rose and stretched myself. My hands and knees still quivered nervously; but I was strong and perfectly well in body. The empty, desolate, tomb-like place was eerie enough to scare any one; but its emptiness was comfort when I thought of its inmates. Then I wandered down the passage towards the fire which was burning in loneliness. Where had the Folk gone? I puzzled over their disappearance.

Suddenly sounds began to break on my ear,

coming from some inner chamber at the end of
that in which the fire burned. I could scarcely
see for the smoke ; but I began to make my way
towards the noise, feeling along the sides of rock.
Then a second gleam of light seemed to rise before
me, and I came to an aperture in the wall which
gave entrance to another room.

This in turn was full of smoke and glow—a
murky orange glow, as if from some strange flame
of roots. There were the squat moving figures,
running in wild antics round the fire. I crouched
in the entrance, terrified and yet curious, till I
saw something beyond the blaze which held me
dumb. Apart from the others and tied to some
stake in the wall was a woman's figure, and the
face was the face of the shepherd's sister.

My first impulse was flight. I must get away
and think—plan, achieve some desperate way
of escape. I sped back to the silent chamber
as if the gang were at my heels. It was still
empty, and I stood helplessly in the centre, looking at the impassable walls of rock as a wearied
beast may look at the walls of its cage. I be-
thought me of the way I had escaped before and
rushed thither, only to find it blocked by a huge
contrivance of stone. Yards and yards of solid
rock were between me and the upper air, and yet
through it all came the crash and whistle of the
storm. If I were at my wits' end in this inner
darkness, there was also high commotion among
the powers of the air in that upper world.

As I stood I heard the soft steps of my tor-

mentors. They seemed to think I was medi-
tating escape, for they flung themselves on me
and bore me to the ground. I did not struggle,
and when they saw me quiet, they squatted round
and began to speak. They told me of the holy
season and its sacrifices. At first I could not
follow them ; then when I caught familiar words
I found some clue, and they became intelligible.
They spoke of a woman, and I asked, "What
woman ? " With all frankness they told me of
the custom which prevailed—how every twen-
tieth summer a woman was sacrificed to some
devilish god, and by the hand of one of the stranger
race. I said nothing, but my whitening face
must have told them a tale, though I strove hard
to keep my composure. I asked if they had
found the victims. "She is in this place," they
said ; "and as for the man, thou art he." And
with this they left me.

I had still some hours ; so much I gathered
from their talk, for the sacrifice was at sunset.
Escape was cut off for ever. I have always been
something of a fatalist, and at the prospect of
the irrevocable end my cheerfulness returned.
I had my pistol, for they had taken nothing from
me. I took out the little weapon and fingered
it lovingly. Hope of the lost, refuge of the van-
quished, ease to the coward,—blessed be he who
first conceived it !

The time dragged on, the minutes grew to
hours, and still I was left solitary. Only the mad
violence of the storm broke the quiet. It had

increased in fury, for the stones at the mouth of
the exit by which I had formerly escaped seemed
to rock with some external pressure, and cutting
shafts of wind slipped past and cleft the heat of
the passage. What a sight the ravine outside
must be, I thought, set in the forehead of a great
hill, and swept clean by every blast! Then
came a crashing, and the long hollow echo of a
fall. The rocks are splitting, thought I; the
road down the corrie will be impassable now and
for evermore.

I began to grow weak with the nervousness
of the waiting, and by-and-by I lay down and fell
into a sort of doze. When I next knew consciousness I was being roused by two of the Folk, and
bidden get ready. I stumbled to my feet, felt
for the pistol in the hollow of my sleeve, and
prepared to follow.

When we came out into the wider chamber
the noise of the storm was deafening. The roof
rang like a shield which has been struck. I noticed, perturbed as I was, that my guards cast
anxious eyes around them, alarmed, like myself,
at the murderous din. Nor was the world quieter
when we entered the last chamber, where the fire
burned and the remnant of the Folk waited.
Wind had found an entrance from somewhere or
other, and the flames blew here and there, and
the smoke gyrated in odd circles. At the back,
and apart from the rest, I saw the dazed eyes
and the white old drawn face of the woman.

They led me up beside her to a place where

there was a rude flat stone, hollowed in the centre, and on it a rusty iron knife, which seemed once to have formed part of a scythe blade. Then I saw the ceremonial which was marked out for me. It was the very rite which I had dimly figured as current among a rude people, and even in that moment of horror I had something of the scholar's satisfaction.

The oldest of the Folk, who seemed to be a sort of priest, came to my side and mumbled a form of words. His fetid breath sickened me ; his dull eyes, glassy like a brute's with age, brought my knees together. He put the knife in my hands, dragged the terror-stricken woman forward to the altar, and bade me begin.

I began by sawing her bonds through. When she felt herself free she would have fled back, but stopped when I bade her. At that moment there came a noise of rending and crashing as if the hills were falling, and for one second the eyes of the Folk were averted from the frustrated sacrifice.

Only for a moment. The next they saw what I had done, and with one impulse rushed towards me. Then began the last scene in the play. I sent a bullet through the right eye of the first thing that came on. The second shot went wide ; but the third shattered the hand of an elderly ruffian with a club. Never for an instant did they stop, and now they were clutching at me. I pushed the woman behind, and fired three rapid shots in blind panic, and then, clutching the scythe, I struck right and left like a madman.

Suddenly I saw the foreground sink before my eyes. The roof sloped down, and with a sickening hiss a mountain of rock and earth seemed to precipitate itself on the foremost of my assailants. One, nipped in the middle by a rock, caught my eye by his hideous writhings. Two only remained in what was now a little suffocating chamber, with embers from the fire still smoking on the floor.

The woman caught me by the hand and drew me with her, while the two seemed mute with fear. "There's a road at the back," she screamed. "I ken it. I fand it out." And she pulled me up a narrow hole in the rock.

*　　*　　*　　*　　*　　*

How long we climbed I do not know. We were both fighting for air, with the tightness of throat and chest and the craziness of limb which mean suffocation. I cannot tell when we first came to the surface, but I remember the woman, who seemed to have the strength of extreme terror, pulling me from the edge of a crevasse and laying me on a flat rock. It seemed to be the depth of winter, with sheer-falling rain and a wind that shook the hills.

Then I was once more myself and could look about me. From my feet yawned a sheer abyss, where once had been a hill shoulder. Some great mass of rock on the brow of the mountain had been loosened by the storm, and in its fall had caught the lips of the ravine. For a moment I feared that all had been destroyed.

My feeling—Heaven help me!—was not thank-
fulness for God's mercy and my escape, but a
bitter mad regret. I rushed frantically to the
edge, and when I saw only the blackness of darkness I wept weak tears. All the time the storm
was tearing at my body, and I had to grip hard
by hand and foot to keep my place.

Suddenly on the brink of the ravine I saw a
third figure. We two were not the only fugi-
tives. One of the Folk had escaped.

I ran to it, and to my surprise the thing as
soon as it saw me rushed to meet me. At first
I thought it was with some instinct of self-preser-
vation, but when I saw its eyes I knew the purpose of fight. Clearly one or other should go no
more from the place.

We were some ten yards from the brink when I
grappled with it. Dimly I heard the woman
scream with fright, and saw her scramble across
the hillside. Then we were tugging in a death-
throe, the hideous smell of the thing in my face,
its red eyes burning into mine, and its hoarse
voice muttering. Its strength seemed incredible;
but I, too, am no weakling. We tugged and
strained, its nails biting into my flesh, while I
choked its throat unsparingly. Every second I
dreaded lest we should plunge together over the
ledge, for it was thither my adversary tried to
draw me. I caught my heel in a nick of rock,
and pulled madly against it.

And then, while I was beginning to glory with
the pride of conquest, my hope was dashed in

pieces. The thing seemed to break from my arms, and, as if in despair, cast itself head-long into the impenetrable darkness. I stumbled blindly after it, saved myself on the brink, and fell back into a merciful swoon.

* * * * * *

CHAPTER VIII

NOTE IN CONCLUSION BY THE EDITOR

AT this point the narrative of my unfortunate
friend, Mr. Graves of St. Chad's, breaks off
abruptly. He wrote it shortly before his death,
and was prevented from completing it by the
attack of heart failure which carried him off. In
accordance with the instructions in his will I
have prepared it for publication, and now in much
fear and hesitation give it to the world. First,
however, I must supplement it by such facts as
fall within my knowledge.

The shepherd seems to have gone to Allermuir
and by the help of the letter convinced the in-
habitants. A body of men was collected under
the landlord, and during the afternoon set out
for the hills. But unfortunately the great midsummer storm—the most terrible of recent clima-
tic disturbances—had filled the mosses and streams,
and they found themselves unable to proceed by
any direct road. Ultimately late in the evening
they arrived at the cottage of Farawa, only to
find there a raving woman, the shepherd's sister,
who seemed crazy with brain fever. She told

some rambling story about her escape, but her
narrative said nothing of Mr. Graves. So they
treated her with what skill they possessed, and
sheltered for the night in and around the cottage.
Next morning the storm had abated a little, and
the woman had recovered something of her wits.
From her they learned that Mr. Graves was lying
in a ravine on the side of the Muneraw in immi-
nent danger of his life. A body of men set out
to find him; but so immense was the landslip,
and so dangerous the whole mountain, that it
was nearly evening when they recovered him
from the ledge of rock. He was alive, but unconscious, and on bringing him back to the cottage it was clear that he was indeed very ill.
There he lay for three months, while the best
skill that could be got was procured for him.
By dint of an uncommon toughness of constitu-
tion he survived; but it was an old and feeble
man who returned to Oxford in the early winter.

The shepherd and his sister immediately left the
countryside, and were never more heard of, unless they are the pair of unfortunates who are at
present in a Scottish pauper asylum, incapable of
remembering even their names. The people who
last spoke with them declared that their minds
seemed weakened by a great shock, and that
it was hopeless to try to get any connected or
rational statement.

The career of my poor friend from that hour
was little short of a tragedy. He awoke from his
illness to find the world incredulous; even the

country-folk of Allermuir set down the story to the shepherd's craziness and my friend's credulity. In Oxford his argument was received with polite scorn. An account of his experiences which he drew up for the *Times* was refused by the editor ; and an article on " Primitive Peoples of the North," embodying what he believed to be the result of his discoveries, was rejected by every responsible journal in Europe. At first he bore the treatment bravely. Reflection convinced him that the colony had not been destroyed. Proofs were still awaiting his hand, and with courage and caution he might yet triumph over his enemies. But unfortunately, though the ardour of the scholar burned more fiercely than ever and all fear seemed to have been purged from his soul, the last adventure had grievously sapped his bodily strength. In the spring following his accident he made an effort to reach the spot—alone, for no one could be persuaded to follow him in what was regarded as a childish madness. He slept at the now deserted cottage of Farawa, but in the morning found himself unable to continue, and with difficulty struggled back to the shepherd's cottage at Allercleuch, where he was confined to bed for a fortnight. Then it became necessary for him to seek health abroad, and it was not till the following autumn that he attempted the journey again.

He fell sick a second time at the inn of Allermuir, and during his convalescence had himself carried to a knoll in the inn garden, whence a glimpse can be obtained of the shoulder of the

Muneraw. There he would sit for hours with his eyes fixed on the horizon, and at times he would be found weeping with weakness and vexation. The last attempt was made but two months before his last illness. On this occasion he got no farther than Carlisle, where he was taken ill with what proved to be a premonition of death. After that he shut his lips tightly, as though recognizing the futility of his hopes. Whether he had been soured by the treatment he received, or whether his brain had already been weakened, he had become a morose silent man, and for the two years before his death had few friends and no society. From the obituary notice in the *Times* I take the following paragraph, which shows in what light the world had come to look upon him :—

"At the outset of his career he was regarded as a rising scholar in one department of archæ-ology, and his Taffert lectures were a real con-tribution to an obscure subject. But in after life he was led into fantastic speculations ; and when he found himself unable to convince his colleagues, he gradually retired into himself, and lived practi-cally a hermit's life till his death. His career, thus broken short, is a sad instance of the fascina-tion which the recondite and the quack can exer-cise even over men of approved ability."

And now his own narrative is published, and the world can judge as it pleases about the amaz-ing romance. The view which will doubtless find general acceptance is that the whole is a figment of the brain, begotten of some harmless moorland adventure and the company of such religious maniacs as the shepherd and his sister. But some who knew the former sobriety and calmness of my friend's mind may be disposed timorously and with deep hesitation to another verdict. They may accept the narrative, and believe that somewhere in those moorlands he met with a horrible primitive survival, passed through the strangest adventure, and had his fingers on an epoch-making discovery. In this case they will be inclined to sympathize with the loneliness and misunderstanding of his latter days. It is not for me to decide the question. Though a fellow-historian, the Picts are outside my period, and I dare not advance an opinion on a matter with which I am not fully familiar. But I would point out that the means of settling the question are still extant, and I would call upon some young archæologist, with a reputation to make, to seize upon the chance of the century. Most of the expresses for the North stop at Allerfoot ; a ten-miles' drive will bring him to Allermuir ; and then with a fifteen-miles' walk he is at Farawa and on the threshold of discovery. Let him follow the burn and cross the ridge and ascend the Scarts of the Muneraw, and, if he return at all, it may be with a more charitable judgment of my unfortunate friend.

1898.

II

THE FAR ISLANDS

"Lady Alice, Lady Louise,
    Between the wash of the tumbling seas—"

right runs a low beach of sand, passing into rough limestone boulders and then into the pebbles of the wood. This ... is that it bounded by a reef of low rocks falling ever-and-anon to this water's edge. It is ... with a fringe of heath and ... length of short ... with ... and dwarf pine trees straggling to ... and the low pine ... of its Gaelic name. The Ranger ...

II

ACHILDISH illness sent Colin to Kinlochuna when he had reached the mature age of five, and delicate health kept him there for the greater part of the next six years. During the winter he lived in London, but from the late northern spring, through all the long bright summers, he lived in the great tenantless place without company—for he was an only child. A French nurse had the charge of his doings, and when he had passed through the formality of lessons there were the long pine woods at his disposal, the rough moor, the wonderful black holes with the rich black mud in them, and best of all the bay of Acharra, below the headland, with Cuna lying in the waves a mile to the west. At such times his father was busy elsewhere; his mother was dead; the family had few near relatives; so he passed a solitary childhood in the company of seagulls and the birds of the moor.

His time for the beach was the afternoon. On the left as you go down through the woods from the house there runs out the great headland of Acharra, red and grey with mosses, and with a nimbus always of screaming seafowl. To the right runs a low beach of sand, passing into rough limestone boulders and then into the heather of the wood. This in turn is bounded by a reef of low rocks falling by gentle breaks to the water's edge. It is crowned with a tangle of heath and fern, bright at most seasons with flowers, and dwarf pine trees straggle on its crest till one sees the meaning of its Gaelic name "The Ragged Cockscomb." This place was Colin's playground in fine weather. When it blew rain or snow from the north he dwelt indoors among dogs and books, puzzling his way through great volumes from his father's shelves. But when the mild west-wind weather fell on the sea, then he would lie on the hot sand—Amèlie the nurse reading a novel on the nearest rock—and kick his small heels as he followed his fancy. He built great sand castles to the shape of Acharra old tower, and peopled them with preposterous knights and ladies; he drew great moats and rivers for the tide to fill; he fought battles innumerable with crackling sea-weed, till Amèlie, with her sharp cry of "Colín, Colín," would carry him houseward for tea.

Two fancies remained in his mind through those boyish years. One was about the mysterious shining sea before him. In certain weathers it seemed to him a solid pathway. Cuna, the little ragged isle, ceased to block the horizon, and his own white road ran away down into the west, till suddenly it stopped and he saw no farther. He knew he ought to see more, but always at one place, just when his thoughts were pacing the white

road most gallantly, there came a baffling mist to
his sight, and he found himself looking at a commonplace sea with Cuna lying very real and palpable in the offing. It was a vexatious limitation,
for all his dreams were about this pathway. One
day in June, when the waters slept in a deep heat,
he came down the sands barefoot, and lo! there
was his pathway. For one moment things seemed
clear, the mist had not gathered on the road, and
with a cry he ran down to the tide's edge and
waded in. The touch of water dispelled the illusion, and almost in tears he saw the cruel back
of Cuna blotting out his own magic way.

The other fancy was about the low ridge of
rocks which bounded the bay on the right. His
walks had never extended beyond it, either on
the sands or inland, for that way lay a steep hillside and a perilous bog. But often on the sands
he had come to its foot and wondered what country
lay beyond. He made many efforts to explore it,
difficult efforts, for the vigilant Amèlie had first
to be avoided. Once he was almost at the top
when some seaweed to which he clung gave way,
and he rolled back again to the soft warm sand.
By-and-by he found that he knew what was beyond. A clear picture had built itself up in his
brain of a mile of reefs, with sand in bars between
them, and beyond all a sea-wood of alders slipping
from the hill's skirts to the water's edge. This
was not what he wanted in his explorations, so
he stopped, till one day it struck him that the
westward view might reveal something beyond

the hog-backed Cuna. One day, pioneering alone, he scaled the steepest heights of the seaweed and pulled his chin over the crest of the ridge. There, sure enough, was his picture—a mile of reefs and the tattered sea-wood. He turned eagerly sea-wards. Cuna still lay humped on the waters, but beyond it he seemed to see his shining pathway running far to a speck which might be an island. Crazy with pleasure he stared at the vision, till slowly it melted into the waves, and Cuna the inexorable once more blocked the sky-line. He climbed down, his heart in a doubt between des-pondency and hope.

It was the last day of such fancies, for on the morrow he had to face the new world of school.

*   *   *   *   *   *

At Cecil's Colin found a new life and a thou-sand new interests. His early delicacy had been driven away by the sea winds of Acharra, and he was rapidly growing up a tall, strong child, straight of limb like all his house, but sinewy and alert beyond his years. He learned new games with astonishing facility, became a fast bowler with a genius for twists, and a Rugby three-quarters full of pluck and cunning. He soon attained to the modified popularity of a private school, and, being essentially clean, strong, and healthy, found himself a mark for his juniors' worship and a favourite with masters. The homage did not spoil him, for no boy was ever less self-pos-sessed. On the cricket ground and the football field he was a leader, but in private he had the nervous, sensitive manners of the would-be recluse. No one ever accused him of "side"—his polite, halting address was the same to junior and senior; and the result was that wild affection which simplicity in the great is wont to inspire. He spoke with a pure accent, in which lurked no northern trace; in a little he had forgotten all about his birthplace and his origin. His name had at first acquired for him the sobriquet of "Scottie," but the title was soon dropped from its manifest ineptness.

In his second year at Cecil's he caught a prevalent fever, and for days lay very near the brink of death. At his worst he was wildly delirious, crying ceaselessly for Acharra and the beach at Kinlochuna. But as he grew convalescent the absorption remained, and for the moment he seemed to have forgotten his southern life. He found himself playing on the sands, always with the boundary ridge before him, and the hump of Cuna rising in the sea. When dragged back to his environment by the inquiries of Bellew, his special friend, who came to sit with him, he was so abstracted and forgetful that the good Bellew was seriously grieved. "The chap's a bit cracked, you know," he announced in hall. "Didn't know me. Asked me what 'footer' meant when I told him about the Bayswick match, and talked about nothing but a lot of heathen Scotch names."

One dream haunted Colin throughout the days of his recovery. He was tormented with a furious thirst, poorly assuaged at long intervals by watered milk. So when he crossed the borders of dreamland his first search was always for a well. He tried the brushwood inland from the beach, but it was dry as stone. Then he climbed with difficulty the boundary ridge, and found little pools of salt water, while far on the other side gleamed the dark black bog-holes. Here was not what he sought, and he was in deep despair, till suddenly over the sea he caught a glimpse of his old path running beyond Cuna to a bank of mist. He rushed down to the tide's edge, and to his amazement found solid ground. Now was the chance for which he had long looked, and he ran happily westwards, till of a sudden the solid earth seemed to sink with him, and he was in the waters struggling. But two curious things he noted. One was that the far bank of mist seemed to open for a pin-point of time, and he had a gleam of land. He saw nothing distinctly, only a line which was not mist and was not water. The second was that the water was fresh, and as he was drinking from this curious new fresh sea he awoke. The dream was repeated three times before he left the sick-room. Always he wakened at the same place, always he quenched his thirst in the fresh sea, but never again did the mist open for him, and show him the strange country.

*   *   *   *   *   *

From Cecil's he went to the famous school which was the tradition in his family. The Head spoke to his house-master of his coming. "We are to have another Raden here," he said, "and

I am glad of it, if the young one turns out to be
anything like the others. There's a good deal
of dry-rot among the boys just now. They are
all too old for their years and too wise in the
wrong way. They haven't anything like the
enthusiasm in games they had twenty years ago
when I first came here. I hope this young Raden
will stir them up." The house-master agreed,
and when he first caught sight of Colin's slim,
well-knit figure, looked into the handsome kindly
eyes, and heard his curiously diffident speech,
his doubts vanished. "We have got the right
stuff now," he told himself, and the senior
for whom the new boy fagged made the same
comment.

From the anomalous insignificance of fagdom
Colin climbed up the School, leaving everywhere
a record of honest good-nature. He was allowed
to forget his cricket and football, but in return he
was initiated into the mysteries of the river.
Water had always been his delight, so he went
through the dreary preliminaries of being coached
in a tub-pair till he learned to swing steadily
and get his arms quickly forward. Then came
the stages of scratch fours and scratch eights,
till after a long apprenticeship he was promoted
to the dignity of a thwart in the Eight itself.
In his last year he was Captain of Boats, a position which joins the responsibility of a Cabinet
Minister to the rapturous popular applause of a
successful warrior. Nor was he the least distinguished of a great band. With Colin at seven the

School won the Ladies' after the closest race on record.

The Head's prophecy fell true, for Colin was a born leader. For all his good-humour and diffidence of speech, he had a trick of shutting his teeth which all respected. As captain he was the idol of the school, and he ruled it well and justly. For the rest, he was a curious boy with none of the ordinary young enthusiasms, reserved for all his kindliness. At house "shouters" his was not the voice which led the stirring strains of "Stroke out all you know," though his position demanded it. He cared little about work, and the Schoolhouse scholar, who fancied him from his manner a devotee of things intellectual, found in Colin but an affected interest. He read a certain amount of modern poetry with considerable boredom; fiction he never opened. The truth was that he had a romance in his own brain which, willy nilly, would play itself out, and which left him small relish for the pale second-hand inanities of art. Often, when with others he would lie in the deep meadows by the river on some hot summer's day, his fancies would take a curious colour. He adored the soft English landscape, the lush grasses, the slow streams, the ancient secular trees. But as he looked into the hazy green distance a colder air would blow on his cheek, a pungent smell of salt and pines would be for a moment in his nostrils, and he would be gazing at a line of waves on a beach, a ridge of low rocks, and a shining sea-path running out

was the whole desire of life, the Golden City, the Far Islands, whatever you care to call it." Colin shivered, as if his holy places had been profaned, set down the man in his mind most unjustly as an "awful little cad," and hurried him back to the house.

* * * * * *

Oxford received the boy with open arms, for his reputation had long preceded him. To the majority of men he was the one freshman of his year, and gossip was busy with his prospects. Nor was gossip disappointed. In his first year he rowed seven in the Eight. The next year he was captain of his college boats, and a year later the O.U.B.C. made him its president. For three years he rowed in the winning Eight, and old coaches agreed that in him the perfect seven had been found. It was he who in the famous race of 18— caught up in the last three hundred yards the quickened stroke which gave Oxford victory. As he grew to his full strength he became a splendid figure of a man—tall, supple, deep-chested for all his elegance. His quick dark eyes and his kindly hesitating manners made people think his face extraordinarily handsome, when really it was in no way above the common. But his whole figure, as he stood in his shorts and sweater on the raft at Putney, was so full of youth and strength that people involuntarily smiled when they saw him—a smile of pleasure in so proper a piece of manhood.

Colin enjoyed life hugely at Oxford, for to one

so frank and well-equipped the place gave of its
best. He was the most distinguished personage
of his day there, but, save to school friends and
the men he met officially on the river, he was little
known. His diffidence and his very real exclu-
siveness kept him from being the centre of a host
of friends. His own countrymen in the place
were utterly nonplussed by him. They claimed
him eagerly as a fellow, but he had none of the
ordinary characteristics of the race. There were
Scots of every description around him—pale-
faced Scots who worked incessantly, metaphysi-
cal Scots who talked in the Union, robustious
Scots who played football. They were all men
of hearty manners and many enthusiasms—who
quoted Burns and dined to the immortal bard's
honour every 25th of January ; who told inter-
minable Scotch stories, and fell into fervours over
national sports, dishes, drinks, and religions.
To the poor Colin it was all inexplicable. At
the remote house of Kinlochuna he had never
heard of a Free Kirk or a haggis. He had never
read a line of Burns, Scott bored him exceedingly,
and in all honesty he thought Scots sports inferior
to southern games. He had no great love for the
bleak country, he cared nothing for the traditions
of his house, so he was promptly set down by his
compatriots as " denationalized and degenerate."

He was idle, too, during these years as far as
his " schools " were concerned, but he was always
very intent upon his own private business. When-
ever he sat down to read, when he sprawled on

the grass at river picnics, in chapel, in lecture—
in short, at any moment when his body was at
rest and his mind at leisure—his fancies were off
on the same old path. Things had changed,
however, in that country. The boyish device
of a hard road running over the waters had gone,
and now it was invariably a boat which he saw
beached on the shingle. It differed in shape.
At first it was an ugly salmon coble, such as the
fishermen used for the nets at Kinlochuna. Then
it passed, by rapid transitions, through a canvas
skiff which it took good watermanship to sit,
a whiff, an ordinary dinghy, till at last it settled
itself into a long rough boat, pointed at both ends,
with oar-holes in the sides instead of rowlocks.
It was the devil's own business to launch it, and
launch it anew he was compelled to for every
journey; for though he left it bound in a little
rock hollow below the ridge after landing, yet
when he returned, lo! there was the clumsy thing
high and dry upon the beach.

The odd point about the new venture was
that Cuna had ceased to trouble him. As soon
as he had pulled his first stroke the island disappeared, and nothing lay before him but the
sea fog. Yet, try as he might, he could come
little nearer. The shores behind him might sink
and lessen, but the impenetrable mist was still
miles to the westward. Sometimes he rowed so
far that the shore was a thin line upon the horizon, but when he turned the boat it seemed to
ground in a second on the beach. The long

laboured journey out and the instantaneous
return puzzled him at first, but soon he became
used to them. His one grief was the mist, which
seemed to grow denser as he neared it. The sudden glimpse of land which he had got from the
ridge of rock in the old boyish days was now
denied him, and with the denial came a keener
exultation in the quest. Somewhere in the west,
he knew, must be land, and in this land a well
of sweet water—for so he had interpreted his
feverish dream. Sometimes when the wind blew
against him, he caught scents from it—generally
the scent of pines, on the little ridge on the shore
behind him.

One day on his college barge, while he was
waiting for a picnic party to start, he seemed
to get nearer than before. Out on that western
sea, as he saw it, it was fresh, blowing weather,
with a clear hot sky above. It was hard work
rowing, for the wind was against him, and the
sun scorched his forehead. The air seemed full
of scents—and sounds, too, sounds of far-away
surf and wind in trees. He rested for a moment
on his oars and turned his head. His heart
beat quickly, for there was a rift in the mist,
and far through a line of sand ringed with snow-
white foam.

Somebody shook him roughly: "Come on,
Colin, old man. They're all waiting for you.
Do you know you've been half asleep?"

Colin rose and followed silently, with drowsy
eyes. His mind was curiously excited. He had

looked inside the veil of mist. Now he knew
what was the land he sought.

*   *   *   *   *   *

He made the voyage often, now that the spell
was broken. It was short work to launch the
boat, and, whereas it had been a long pull formerly,
now it needed only a few strokes to bring him to
the Rim of the Mist. There was no chance of
getting farther, and he scarcely tried. He was
content to rest there, in a world of curious scents
and sounds, till the mist drew down and he was
driven back to shore.

The change in his environment troubled him
little. For a man who has been an idol at the
University to fall suddenly into the comparative
insignificance of Town is often a bitter experience ;
but Colin, whose thoughts were not ambitious,
scarcely noticed it. He found that he was less
his own master than before, but he humbled himself to his new duties without complaint. Many
of his old friends were about him ; he had plenty
of acquaintances ; and, being sufficient unto himself, he was unaccustomed to ennui. Invitations
showered upon him thick and fast. Match-making
mothers, knowing his birth and his father's income,
and reflecting that he was the only child of his
house, desired him as a son-in-law. He was bidden
welcome everywhere, and the young girls, for whose
sake he was thus courted, found in him an attract-
ive mystery. The tall good-looking athlete, with
the kind eyes and the preposterously nervous manner, wakened their maidenly sympathies. As they

danced with him or sat next to him at dinner, they talked fervently of Oxford, of the north, of the army, of his friends. "Stupid, but nice, my dear," was Lady Afflint's comment; and Miss Claire Etheridge, the beauty of the year, declared to her friends that he was a "dear boy, but so awkward." He was always forgetful, and ever apologetic; and when he forgot the Shandwicks' theatre party, the Herapaths' dance, and at least a dozen minor matters, he began to acquire the reputation of a cynic and a recluse.

"You're a queer chap, Col," Lieutenant Bellew said in expostulation.

Colin shrugged his shoulders; he was used to the description.

"Do you know that Claire Etheridge was trying all she knew to please you this afternoon, and you looked as if you weren't listening? Most men would have given their ears to be in your place."

"I'm awfully sorry, but I thought I was very polite to her."

"And why weren't you at the Marshams' show?"

"Oh, I went to polo with Collinson and another man. And, I say, old chap, I'm not coming to the Logans to-morrow. I've got a fence on with Adair at the school."

Little Bellew, who was a tremendous mirror of fashion and chevalier in general, looked up curiously at his tall friend.

"Why don't you like the women, Col, when they're so fond of you?"

"They aren't," said Colin hotly, "and I don't dislike 'em. But, Lord! they bore me. I might be doing twenty things when I talk nonsense to one of 'em for an hour. I come back as stupid as an owl, and besides, there's heaps of things better sport."

The truth was that, while among men he was a leader and at his ease, among women his psychic balance was so oddly upset that he grew nervous and returned unhappy. The boat on the beach, ready in general to appear at the slightest call, would delay long after such experiences, and its place would be taken by some woman's face for which he cared not a straw. For the boat, on the other hand, he cared a very great deal. In all his frank wholesome existence there was this enchanting background, this pleasure garden which he cherished more than anything in life. He had come of late to look at it with somewhat different eyes. The eager desire to search behind the mist was ever with him, but now he had also some curiosity about the details of the picture. As he pulled out to the Rim of the Mist sounds seemed to shape themselves on his lips, which by-and-by grew into actual words in his memory. He wrote them down in scraps, and after some sorting they seemed to him a kind of Latin. He remembered a college friend of his, one Medway, now reading for the Bar, who had been the foremost scholar of his acquaintance; so with the scrap of paper in his pocket he climbed one evening to Medway's rooms in the Temple.

The man read the words curiously, and puzzled
for a bit. " What's made you take to Latin comps
so late in life, Colin ? It's baddish, you know,
even for you. I thought they'd have licked more
into you at Eton."

Colin grinned with amusement. " I'll tell you
about it later," he said. " Can you make out
what it means ? "

" It seems to be a kind of dog-Latin or monkish
Latin or something of the sort," said Medway.
" It reads like this : ' *Soles occidere solent* ' (that's
cribbed from Catullus, and besides it's the regular
monkish pun) . . . *qua* . . . then *blandula* something. Then there's a lot of Choctaw, and then
*illæ insulæ dilectæ in quas festinant somnia animulæ
gaudia*. That's pretty fair rot. Hullo, by George !
here's something better—*Insula pomorum insula
vitæ*. That's Geoffrey of Monmouth."

He made a dive to a bookcase and pulled out
a battered little calf-bound duodecimo. " Here's
all about your Isle of Apple-trees. Listen. ' Sit-
uate far out in the Western ocean, beyond the
Utmost Islands, beyond even the little Isle of
Sheep where the cairns of dead men are, lies the
Island of Apple-trees where the heroes and princes
of the nations live their second life.' " He closed
the book and put it back. " It's the old ancient
story, the Greek Hesperides, the British Avilion,
and this Apple-tree Island is the northern equiva-
lent."

Colin sat entranced, his memory busy with a
problem. Could he distinguish the scent of apple

trees among the perfumes of the Rim of the Mist. For the moment he thought he could. He was roused by Medway's voice asking the story of the writing.

"Oh, it's just some nonsense that was running in my head, so I wrote it down to see what it was."

"But you must have been reading. A new exercise for you, Colin!"

"No, I wasn't reading. Look here. You know the sort of pictures you make for yourself of places you like."

"Rather! Mine is a Yorkshire moor with a little grey shooting-box in the heart of it."

"Well, mine is different. Mine is a sort of beach with a sea and a lot of islands somewhere far out. It is a jolly place, fresh, you know, and blowing, and smells good. 'Pon my word, now I think of it, there's always been a scent of apples."

"Sort of cider-press? Well, I must be off. You'd better come round to the club and see the telegrams about the war. *You* should be keen about it."

One evening, a week later, Medway met a friend called Tillotson at the club, and, being lonely, they dined together. Tillotson was a man of some note in science, a dabbler in psychology, an amateur historian, a ripe genealogist. They talked of politics and the war, of a new book, of Mrs. Runnymede, and finally of their hobbies.

"I am writing an article," said Tillotson. "Craikes asked me to do it for the *Monthly*. It's on a nice point in psychics. I call it 'The

Transmission of Fallacies,' but I do not mean the
logical kind. The question is, Can a particular
form of hallucination run in a family for generations ? The proof must, of course, come from my
genealogical studies. I maintain it can. I instance the Douglas-Ernotts, not one of whom can
see straight with the left eye. That is one side.
In another class of examples I take the Drapiers,
who hate salt water and never go on board ship
if they can help it. Then you remember the
Durwards ? Old Lady Balcrynie used to tell
me that no one of the lot could ever stand the
sight of a green frock. There's a chance for the
romancer. The Manorwaters have the same madness, only their colour is red."

A vague remembrance haunted Medway's brain.

" I know a man who might give you points
from his own case. Did you ever meet a man
Raden—Colin Raden ? "

Tillotson nodded. " Long chap—in the Guards ?
'Varsity oar, and rather a useful bowler ? No, I
don't know him. I know him well by sight, and
I should like to meet him tremendously—as a
genealogist, of course."

" Why ? " asked Medway.

" Why ? Because the man's family is unique.
You never hear much about them nowadays, but
away up in that north-west corner of Scotland
they have ruled since the days of Noah. Why,
man, they were aristocrats when our Howards and
Nevilles were greengrocers. I wish you would get
this Raden to meet me some night."

"I am afraid there's no chance of it just at present," said Medway, taking up an evening paper. "I see that his battalion has gone to the front. But remind me when he comes back, and I'll be delighted."

III

III

AND now there began for Colin a curious divided life—without, a constant shifting of scene, days of heat and bustle and toil; within, a slow, tantalizing, yet exquisite adventure. The Rim of the Mist was now no more the goal of his journeys, but the starting-point. Lying there, amid cool, fragrant sea winds, his fanciful ear was subtly alert for the sounds of the dim land before him. Sleeping and waking the quest haunted him. As he flung himself on his bed the kerosene-filled air would change to an ocean freshness, the old boat would rock beneath him, and with clear eye and a boyish hope he would be waiting and watching. And then suddenly he would be back on shore, Cuna and the Acharra headland shining grey in the morning light, and with gritty mouth and sand-filled eyes he would awaken to the heat of the desert camp.

He was kept busy, for his good-humour and energy made him a willing slave, and he was ready enough for volunteer work when others were weak with heat and despair. A thirty-mile ride left him untired; more, he followed the campaign with a sharp intelligence and found a new

enthusiasm for his profession. Discomforts there
might be, but the days were happy; and then—
the cool land, the bright land, which was his for
the thinking of it.

Soon they gave him reconnoitring work to do,
and his wits were put to the trial. He came well
out of the thing, and earned golden praise from
the silent colonel in command. He enjoyed it as
he had enjoyed a hard race on the river or a good
cricket match, and when his worried companions
marvelled at his zeal he stammered and grew
uncomfortable.

"How the deuce do you keep it up, Colin?"
the major asked him. "I'm an old hand at the
job, and yet I've got a temper like devilled bones.
You seem as chirpy as if you were going out to
fish a chalk-stream on a June morning."

"Well, the fact is—" and Colin pulled himself
up short, knowing that he could never explain.
He felt miserably that he had an unfair advantage
of the others. Poor Bellew, who groaned and swore
in the heat at his side, knew nothing of the Rim of
the Mist. It was rough luck on the poor beggars,
and who but himself was the fortunate man?

As the days passed a curious thing happened.
He found fragments of the other world straying
into his common life. The barriers of the two
domains were falling, and more than once he
caught himself looking at a steel-blue sea when his
eyes should have found a mustard-coloured desert.
One day, on a reconnoitring expedition, they
stopped for a little on a hillock above a jungle of

scrub, and, being hot and tired, scanned listlessly
the endless yellow distances.

"I suppose yon hill is about ten miles off," said
Bellew with dry lips.

Colin looked vaguely. "I should say five."

"And what's that below it—the black patch?
Stones or scrub?"

Colin was in a day-dream. "Why do you call
it black? It's blue, quite blue."

"Rot," said the other. "It's grey-black."

"No, it's water with the sun shining on it. It's
blue, but just at the edges it's very near sea-green."

Bellew rose excitedly. "Hullo, Col, you're seeing the mirage! And you the fittest of the lot of
us! You've got the sun in your head, old man!"

"Mirage!" Colin cried in contempt. He was
awake now, but the thought of confusing his own
bright western sea with a mirage gave him a
curious pain. For a moment he felt the gulf of
separation between his two worlds, but only for
a moment. As the party remounted he gave his
fancies the rein, and ere he reached camp, he had
felt the oars in his hand and sniffed the apple-tree
blossom from the distant beaches.

The major came to him after supper.

"Bellew told me you were a bit odd to-day,
Colin," he said. "I expect your eyes are getting
baddish. Better get your sand-spectacles out."

Colin laughed. "Thanks. It's awfully good of
you to bother, but I think Bellew took me up
wrong. I never was fitter in my life."

*   *   *   *   *   *

By-and-by the turn came for pride to be humbled. A low desert fever took him, and though he went through the day as usual, it was with dreary lassitude ; and at night, with hot hands clasped above his damp hair, he found sleep a hard goddess to conquer.

It was the normal condition of the others, so he had small cause to complain, but it worked havoc with his fancies. He had never been ill since his childish days, and this little fever meant much to one whose nature was poised on a needle-point. He found himself confronted with a hard bare world, with the gilt rubbed from its corners. The Rim of the Mist seemed a place of vague horrors ; when he reached it his soul was consumed with terror ; he struggled impotently to advance ; behind him Cuna and the Acharra coast seemed a place of evil dreams. Again, as in his old fever, he was tormented with a devouring thirst, but the sea beside him was not fresh, but brackish as a rock-pool. He yearned for the apple-tree beaches in front ; there, he knew, were cold springs of water ; the fresh smell of it was blown towards him in his nightmare.

But as the days passed and the misery for all grew more intense, an odd hope began to rise in his mind. It could not last, coolness and health were waiting near, and his reason for the hope came from the odd events at the Rim of the Mist. The haze was clearing from the foreground, the surf-lined coast seemed nearer, and though all was obscure save the milk-white sand and the foam, yet that was earnest enough for him. Once more he became cheerful; weak and light-headed he rode out again; and the major, who was recovering from sunstroke, found envy take the place of pity in his soul.

The hope was near fulfilment. One evening when the heat was changing into the cooler twilight, Colin and Bellew were sent with a small picked body to scour the foothills above the river in case of a flank attack during the night march. It was work they had done regularly for weeks, and it is possible that precautions were relaxed. At any rate, as they turned a corner of hill, in a sandy pass where barren rocks looked down on more barren thorn thickets, a couple of rifle-shots rang out from the scarp, and above them appeared a line of dark faces and white steel. A mere handful, taken at a disadvantage, they could not hope to disperse numbers, so Colin gave the word to wheel about and return. Again shots rang out, and little Bellew had only time to catch at his friend's arm to save him from falling from the saddle.

The word of command had scarcely left Colin's mouth when a sharp pain went through his chest, and his breath seemed to catch and stop. He felt as in a condensed moment of time the heat, the desert smell, the dust in his eyes and throat, while he leaned helplessly forward on his horse's mane. Then the world vanished for him. . . . The boat was rocking under him, the oars in his hand. He pulled and it moved, straight, arrow-like towards the forbidden shore. As if under a great wind the mist furled up and fled. Scents of pines, of apple trees, of great fields of thyme and heather, hung about him ; the sound of wind in a forest, of cool waters falling in showers, of old moorland music, came thin and faint with an exquisite clearness. A second and the boat was among the surf, its gunwale ringed with white foam, as it leaped to the still waters beyond. Clear and deep and still the water lay, and then the white beaches shelved downward, and the boat grated on the sand. He turned, every limb alert with a strange new life, crying out words which had shaped themselves on his lips and which an echo seemed to catch and answer. There were the green forests before him, the hills of peace, the cold white waters. With a passionate joy he leaped on the beach, his arms outstretched to this new earth, this light of the world, this old desire of the heart—youth, rapture, immortality.

*　　*　　*　　*　　*　　*

Bellew brought the body back to camp, himself half-dead with fatigue and whimpering like a child. He almost fell from his horse, and when others took his burden from him and laid it reverently in his tent, he stood beside it, rubbing sand and sweat from his poor purblind eyes, his teeth chattering with fever. He was given something to drink, but he swallowed barely a mouthful.

" It was some d-d-damned sharpshooter," he said. " Right through the breast, and he never spoke to me again. My poor old Col! He was the best chap God ever created, and I do-don't care a dash what becomes of me now. I was at school with him, you know, you men."

"Was he killed outright?" asked the major hoarsely.

"N-no. He lived for about five minutes. But I think the sun had got into his head or he was mad with pain, for he d-d-didn't know where he was. He kept crying out about the smell of pine trees and heather and a lot of pure nonsense about water."

"*Et dulces reminiscitur Argos*," somebody quoted mournfully, as they went out to the desert evening.

1892.

dred years, the few wayside houses were toll-bars or defunct hostelries. The names, too, were great—Scots baronial with a smack of France—Chatelray and Reiverslaw, Black Holm and Champertoun. The place had a cunning charm, mystery dwelt in every cranny, and yet it did not please me. The earth smelt heavy and raw, the roads were red underfoot, all was old, sorrowful, and uncanny. Compared with the fresh Highland glen I had left, where wind and sun and flying showers were never absent, all was chilly and dull and dead. Even when the sun sent a shiver of crimson over the crests of certain firs, I felt no delight in the prospect. I admitted shamefacedly to myself that I was in a very bad temper.

I had been staying at Glenaicill with the Clanroydens, and for a week had found the proper pleasure in life. You know the house with its old rooms and gardens, and the miles of heather which defend it from the world. The shooting had been extraordinary for a wild place far on in the season, for there are few partridges and the woodcock are notoriously late. I had done respectably in my stalking, more than respectably on the river, and creditably on the moors. Moreover, there were pleasant people in the house—and there were the Clanroydens. I had had a hard year's work, sustained to the last moment of term, and a fortnight in Norway had been disastrous. It was therefore with real comfort that I had settled myself down for another ten days in Glenaicill, when all my plans were shattered by Sybil's letter.

Sybil is my cousin and my very good friend, and in old days when I was briefless I had fallen in love with her many times. But she very sensibly chose otherwise, and married a man Ladlaw —Robert John Ladlaw—who had been at school with me. He was a cheery, good-humoured fellow, a great sportsman, a justice of the peace and deputy-lieutenant for his county, and something of an antiquary in a mild way. He had a box in Leicestershire to which he went in the hunting season ; but from February till October he lived in his moorland home. The place was called the House of More, and I had shot there once or twice in recent years. I remembered its loneliness and its comfort, the charming diffident Sybil and Ladlaw's genial welcome. And my recollections set me puzzling again over the letter which that morning had broken into my comfort. " You promised us a visit this autumn," Sybil had written, " and I wish you would come as soon as you can." So far common politeness. But she had gone on to reveal the fact that Ladlaw was ill, she did not know what exactly, but something, she thought, to do with his heart. Then she had signed herself my affectionate cousin, and then had come a short violent postscript, in which, as it were, the fences of convention had been laid low. " For Heaven's sake come and see us ! " she scrawled below. " Bob is terribly ill. and I am crazy. Come at once." And then she finished with an afterthought, "Don't bother about bringing doctors. It is not their business."

She had assumed that I would come, and dutifully I set out. I could not regret my decision, but I took leave to upbraid my luck. The thought of Glenaicill with the woodcock beginning to arrive, and the Clanroydens imploring me to stay, saddened my journey in the morning, and the murky, coally midland country of the afternoon completed my depression. The drive through the woodlands of More failed to raise my spirits. I was anxious about Sybil and Ladlaw, and this accursed country had always given me a certain eeriness on my first approaching it. You may call it silly; but I have no nerves, and am little susceptible to vague sentiment. It was sheer physical dislike of the rich deep soil, the woody and antique smells, the melancholy roads and trees, and the flavour of old mystery. I am aggressively healthy and wholly Philistine. I love clear outlines and strong colours, and More, with its half-tints and hazy distances, depressed me miserably. Even when the road crept uphill and the trees ended, I found nothing to hearten me in the moorland which succeeded. It was genuine moorland, close on 800 feet above the sea, and through it ran this old grass-grown coach-road. Low hills rose to the left, and to the right after some miles of peat flared the chimneys of pits and oil-works. Straight in front the moor ran out into the horizon, and there in the centre was the last dying spark of the sun. The place

was as still as the grave save for the crunch of our
wheels on the grassy road ; but the flaring lights
to the north seemed to endow it with life. I
have rarely felt so keenly the feeling of movement
in the inanimate world. It was an unquiet place,
and I shivered nervously. Little gleams of loch
came from the hollows, the burns were brown
with peat, and every now and then there rose
in the moor jags of sickening red stone.

I remembered that Ladlaw had talked about
the place as the old Manann, the holy land of the
ancient races. I had paid little attention at the
time, but now it struck me that the old peoples
had been wise in their choice. There was something uncanny in this soil and air. Framed in
dank mysterious woods, and a country of coal
and ironstone, no great distance, too, from the
capital city, it was a sullen relic of a lost barbarism. Over the low hills lay a green pastoral
country with bright streams and valleys, but
here in this peaty desert there were few sheep
and little cultivation. The House of More was
the only dwelling, and, save for the ragged village, the wilderness was given over to the wild
things of the hills. The shooting was good ;
but the best shooting on earth would not per-
suade me to make my abode in such a place.
Ladlaw was ill ; well, I did not wonder. You
can have uplands without air, moors that are
not health-giving, and a country life which is
more arduous than a townsman's. I shivered
again, for I seemed to have passed in a few

hours from the open noon to a kind of dank twilight.

We passed the village and entered the lodge gates. Here there were trees again, little innocent new-planted firs, which flourished badly. Some large plane trees grew near the house, and there were thickets upon thickets of the ugly elder. Even in the half-darkness I could see that the lawns were trim and the flower-beds respectable for the season ; doubtless Sybil looked after the gardeners. The oblong whitewashed house, more like a barrack than ever, opened suddenly on my sight, and I experienced my first sense of comfort since I left Glenaicill. Here I should find warmth and company, and, sure enough, the hall door was wide open, and in the great flood of light which poured from it Sybil stood to welcome me.

She ran down the steps as I dismounted, and, with a word to the groom, caught my arm and drew me into the shadow. "O Henry, it was so good of you to come. You mustn't let Bob think that you know he is ill. We don't talk about it. I'll tell you afterwards. I want you to cheer him up. Now we must go in, for he is in the hall expecting you."

While I stood blinking in the light, Ladlaw came forward with outstretched hand and his usual cheery greeting. I looked at him and saw nothing unnatural in his appearance : a little drawn at the lips, perhaps, and heavy below the eyes, but still fresh-coloured and healthy. It was Sybil who showed change. She was very pale, her pretty eyes were deplorably mournful, and in place of her delightful shyness there was the self-confidence and composure of pain. I was honestly shocked, and as I dressed my heart was full of hard thoughts about Ladlaw. What could his illness mean? He seemed well and cheerful, while Sybil was pale, and yet it was Sybil who had written the postscript. As I warmed myself by the fire, I resolved that this particular family difficulty was my proper business.

II

The Ladlaws were waiting for me in the drawing-room. I noticed something new and strange in Sybil's demeanour. She looked to her husband with a motherly protective air, while Ladlaw, who had been the extreme of masculine independence, seemed to cling to his wife with a curious appealing fidelity. In conversation he did little more than echo her words. Till dinner was announced he spoke of the weather, the shooting, and Mabel Clanroyden. Then he did a queer thing, for, when I was about to offer my arm to Sybil, he forestalled me, and, clutching her right arm with his left hand, led the way to the dining-room, leaving me to follow in some bewilderment.

I have rarely taken part in a more dismal meal. The House of More has a pretty Georgian panelling through most of the rooms; but in the

dining-room the walls are level, and painted a
dull stone colour. Abraham offered up Isaac in
a ghastly picture in front of me. Some photographs of the Quorn hung over the mantelpiece,
and five or six drab ancestors filled up the remaining space. But one thing was new and startling.
A great marble bust, a genuine antique, frowned
on me from a pedestal. The head was in the late
Roman style, clearly of some emperor, and in
its commonplace environment the great brows,
the massive neck, and the mysterious, solemn
lips had a surprising effect. I nodded towards
the thing, and asked what it represented.

Ladlaw grunted something which I took for
"Justinian," but he never raised his eyes from
his plate. By accident I caught Sybil's glance.
She looked towards the bust, and laid a finger on
her lips.

The meal grew more doleful as it advanced.
Sybil scarcely touched a dish, but her husband
ate ravenously of everything. He was a strong,
thick-set man, with a square, kindly face, burned
brown by the sun. Now he seemed to have suddenly coarsened. He gobbled with undignified
haste, and his eye was extraordinarily vacant.
A question made him start, and he would turn
on me a face so strange and inert that I repented
the interruption.

I asked him about the autumn's sport, and he
collected his wits with difficulty. He thought
it had been good on the whole, but he had shot
badly. He had not been quite so fit as usual.

No, he had had nobody staying with him—Sybil had wanted to be alone. He was afraid the moor might have been under-shot, but he would make a big day with keepers and farmers before the winter.

"Bob has done pretty well," Sybil said. "He hasn't been out often, for the weather has been very bad here. You can have no idea, Henry, how horrible this moorland place of ours can be when it tries. It is one great sponge sometimes, with ugly red burns, and mud to the ankles."

"I don't think it's healthy," said I.

Ladlaw lifted his face. "Nor do I: I think it's intolerable; but I am so busy, I can't get away."

Once again I caught Sybil's warning eye as I was about to question him on his business.

Clearly the man's brain had received a shock, and he was beginning to suffer from hallucinations. This could be the only explanation, for he had always led a temperate life. The *distrait* wandering manner was the only sign of his malady, for otherwise he seemed normal and mediocre as ever. My heart grieved for Sybil, alone with him in this wilderness.

Then he broke the silence. He lifted his head and looked nervously around till his eye fell on the Roman bust.

"Do you know that this countryside is the old Manann?" he said.

It was an odd turn to the conversation, but I was glad of a sign of intelligence. I answered that I had heard so.

"It's a queer name," he said oracularly ; "but the thing it stood for was queerer. Manann, Manaw," he repeated, rolling the words on his tongue. As he spoke, he glanced sharply, and, as it seemed to me, fearfully, at his left side.

The movement of his body made his napkin slip from his left knee and fall on the floor. It leaned against his leg, and he started from its touch as if he had been stung by a snake. I have never seen a more sheer and transparent terror on a man's face. He got to his feet, his strong frame shaking like a rush. Sybil ran round to his side, picked up the napkin, and flung it on a sideboard. Then she stroked his hair as one would stroke a frightened horse. She called him by his old boy's name of Robin, and at her touch and voice he became quiet. But the particular course then in progress was removed untasted.

In a few minutes he seemed to have forgotten his behaviour, for he took up the former conversation. For a time he spoke well and briskly.

"You lawyers," he said, "understand only the dry framework of the past. You cannot conceive the rapture, which only the antiquary can feel, of constructing in every detail an old culture. Take this Manann. If I could explore the secret of these moors, I would write the world's greatest book. I would write of that prehistoric life when man was knit close to nature. I would describe the people who were brothers of the red earth and the red rock and the red streams of the hills. Oh, it would be horrible, but superb, tremendous! It would be more than a piece of history; it would be a new gospel, a new theory of life. It would kill materialism once and for all. Why, man, all the poets who have deified and personified nature would not do an eighth part of my work. I would show you the unknown, the hideous, shrieking mystery at the back of this simple nature. Men would see the profundity of the old crude faiths which they affect to despise. I would make a picture of our shaggy, sombre-eyed forefather, who heard strange things in the hill silences. I would show him brutal and terror-stricken, but wise, wise, God alone knows how wise! The Romans knew it, and they learned what they could from him, but he did not tell them much. But we have some of his blood in us, and we may go deeper. Manann! A queer land nowadays! I sometimes love it and sometimes hate it, but I always fear it. It is like that statue, inscrutable."

I would have told him that he was talking mystical nonsense; but I had looked towards the bust, and my rudeness was checked on my lips. The moor might be a common piece of ugly waste land, but the statue was inscrutable—of that there was no doubt. I hate your cruel, heavy-mouthed Roman busts; to me they have none of the beauty of life, and little of the interest of art. But my eyes were fastened on this as they had never before looked on marble. The oppression of the heavy woodlands, the mystery of the silent moor, seemed to be caught and held in this face. It was the intangible mystery of culture on the verge of savagery, a cruel, lustful wisdom, and yet a kind of bitter austerity which laughed at the game of life and stood aloof. There was no weakness in the heavy-veined brow and slumbrous eyelids. It was the face of one who had conquered the world and found it dust and ashes, one who had eaten of the tree of the knowledge of good and evil and scorned human wisdom. And at the same time it was the face of one who knew uncanny things, a man who was the intimate of the half-world and the dim background of life. Why on earth I should connect the Roman grandee * with the moorland parish of More, I cannot say; but the fact remains, that there was that in the face which I knew had haunted me through the woodlands and bogs of the place, a sleepless, dismal, incoherent melancholy.

"I bought that at Colenzo's," Ladlaw said, "because it took my fancy. It matches well with this place."

I thought it matched very ill with his drab walls and Quorn photographs, but I held my peace.

"Do you know who it is?" he asked. "It is the head of the greatest man the world has

* I have identified the bust, which, when seen under other circumstances, had little power to affect me. It was a copy of the head of Justinian in the Tesci Museum at Venice, and several duplicates exist, dating apparently from the seventh century, and showing traces of Byzantine decadence in the scrollwork on the hair. It is engraved in M. Delacroix's *Byzantium*, and, I think, in Windscheid's *Pandektenlehrbuch*.

ever seen. You are a lawyer and know you
Justinian."

The Pandects are scarcely part of the dail
work of a common-law barrister. I had no
looked into them since I left college.

"I know that he married an actress," I said
"and was a sort of all-round genius. He mad
law and fought battles and had rows with th
Church. A curious man! And wasn't there
some story about his selling his soul to the Devi
and getting law in exchange? Rather a poo
bargain!"

I chattered away sillily enough, to dispel the
gloom of that dinner-table. The result of my
words was unhappy. Ladlaw gasped, and caught
at his left side as if in pain. Sybil, with tragic
eyes, had been making signs to me to hold my
peace. Now she ran round to her husband's
side and comforted him like a child. As she
passed me she managed to whisper in my ear
to talk to her only and let her husband alone.

For the rest of dinner I obeyed my orders to
the letter. Ladlaw ate his food in gloomy silence,
while I spoke to Sybil of our relatives and friends,
of London, Glenaicill, and any random subject.
The poor girl was dismally forgetful, and her
eye would wander to her husband with wifely
anxiety. I remember being suddenly overcome
by the comic aspect of it all. Here were we
three fools alone in this dank upland, one of us
sick and nervous, talking out-of-the-way nonsense
about Manann and Justinian, gobbling his food

and getting scared at his napkin, another gravely anxious, and myself at my wits' end for a solution. It was a Mad Tea-party with a vengeance, Sybil the melancholy little Dormouse, and Ladlaw the incomprehensible Hatter. I laughed aloud, but checked myself when I caught my cousin's eye. It was really no case for finding humour. Ladlaw was very ill, and Sybil's face was getting deplorably thin.

I welcomed the end of that meal with unmannerly joy, for I wanted to speak seriously with my host. Sybil told the butler to have the lamps lit in the library. Then she leaned over to me and spoke low and rapidly : " I want you to talk to Bob. I'm sure you can do him good. You'll have to be very patient with him and very gentle. Oh, please try and find out what is wrong with him. He won't tell me, and I can only guess."

The butler returned with word that the library was ready to receive us, and Sybil rose to go. Ladlaw half rose, protesting, making the most curious, feeble clutches at his side. His wife quieted him. " Henry will look after you, dear," she said. " You are going into the library to smoke." Then she slipped from the room, and we were left alone.

He caught my arm fiercely with his left hand, and his grip nearly made me cry out. As we walked down the hall I could feel his arm twitching from the elbow to the shoulder. Clearly he was in pain, and I set it down to some form of cardiac affection, which might possibly issue in paralysis.

I settled him in the biggest armchair, and took one of his cigars. The library is the pleasantest room in the house, and at night, when a peat fire burned on the old hearth and the great red curtains were drawn, it used to be the place for comfort and good talk. Now I noticed changes. Ladlaw's book-shelves had been filled with the proceedings of antiquarian societies and many light-hearted works in *belles-lettres*. But now the Badminton Library had been cleared out of a shelf where it stood most convenient to the hand, and its place taken by an old Leyden reprint of Justinian. There were books on Byzantine subjects of which I never dreamed he had heard the names. There were volumes of history and speculation, all of a slightly bizarre kind ; and to crown everything, there were several bulky medical works with gaudily coloured plates. The old atmosphere of sport and travel had gone from the room, with the medley of rods, whips, and gun-cases which used to cumber the tables. Now the place was moderately tidy and slightly learned —and I did not like it.

Ladlaw refused to smoke, and sat for a little while in silence. Then of his own accord he broke the tension—

" It was devilish good of you to come, Harry. This is a lonely place for a man who is a bit seedy."

" I thought you might be alone," I said, " so

I looked you up on my way down from Glenaicill.
I'm sorry to find you looking ill."

" Do you notice it ? " he asked sharply.

" It's tolerably patent," I said. " Have you
seen a doctor ? "

He said something uncomplimentary about
doctors, and kept looking at me with his curious
dull eyes.

I remarked the strange posture in which he
sat—his head screwed round to his right shoulder,
and his whole body a protest against something
at his left hand.

" It looks like your heart," I said. " You
seem to have pains in your left side."

Again a spasm of fear. I went over to him
and stood at the back of his chair.

" Now, for goodness' sake, my dear fellow,
tell me what is wrong ? You're scaring Sybil
to death. It's lonely work for the poor girl,
and I wish you would let me help you."

He was lying back in his chair now, with his
eyes half shut, and shivering like a frightened colt.
The extraordinary change in one who had been
the strongest of the strong kept me from realizing
its gravity. I put a hand on his shoulder, but
he flung it off.

" For God's sake, sit down ! " he said hoarsely.
" I'm going to tell you ; but I'll never make you
understand."

I sat down promptly opposite him.

" It's the Devil," he said very solemnly.

I am afraid that I was rude enough to laugh.

He took no notice, but sat with the same tense, miserable air, staring over my head.

"Right," said I. "Then it is the Devil. It's a new complaint, so it's as well I did not bring a doctor. How does it affect you?"

He made the old impotent clutch at the air with his left hand. I had the sense to become grave at once. Clearly this was some mental affection, some hallucination born of physical pain.

Then he began to talk in a low voice, very rapidly, with his head bent forward like a hunted animal's. I am not going to set down what he told me in his own words, for they were incoherent often, and there was much repetition. But I am going to write the gist of the odd story which took my sleep away on that autumn night, with such explanations and additions as I think needful. The fire died down, the wind arose, the hour grew late, and still he went on in his mumbling recitative. I forgot to smoke, forgot my comfort—everything but the odd figure of my friend and his inconceivable romance. And the night before I had been in cheerful Glenaicill!

*   *   *   *   *   *

He had returned to the House of More, he said, in the latter part of May, and shortly after he fell ill. It was a trifling sickness—influenza or something—but he had never quite recovered. The rainy weather of June depressed him, and the extreme heat of July made him listless and weary. A kind of insistent sleepiness hung over him, and he suffered much from nightmare. To-

wards the end of July his former health returned ;
but he was haunted with a curious oppression.
He seemed to himself to have lost the art of being
alone. There was a perpetual sound in his left
ear, a kind of moving and rustling at his left side,
which never left him by night or day. In addition
he had become the prey of nerves and an insensate
dread of the unknown.

Ladlaw, as I have explained, was a commonplace man, with fair talents, a mediocre culture,
honest instincts, and the beliefs and incredulities
of his class. On abstract grounds I should have
declared him an unlikely man to be the victim of
a hallucination. He had a kind of dull, bourgeois
rationalism, which used to find reasons for all
things in heaven and earth. At first he controlled
his dread with proverbs. He told himself it was
the sequel of his illness, or the light-headedness of
summer heat on the moors. But it soon outgrew
his comfort. It became a living second presence,
an *alter ego* which dogged his footsteps. He became acutely afraid of it. He dared not be alone
for a moment, and clung to Sybil's company
despairingly. She went off for a week's visit in
the beginning of August, and he endured for seven
days the tortures of the lost. His malady advanced upon him with swift steps. The presence
became more real daily. In the early dawning,
in the twilight, and in the first hours of the morning it seemed at times to take a visible bodily
form. A kind of amorphous featureless shadow
would run from his side into the darkness, and

he would sit palsied with terror. Sometimes in lonely places his footsteps sounded double, and something would brush elbows with him. Human society alone exorcised it. With Sybil at his side he was happy; but as soon as she left him the thing came slinking back from the unknown to watch by him. Company might have saved him, but joined to his affliction was a crazy dread of his fellows. He would not leave his moorland home, but must bear his burden alone among the wild streams and mosses of that dismal place.

The Twelfth came, and he shot wretchedly, for his nerve had gone to pieces. He stood exhaustion badly, and became a dweller about the doors. But with this bodily inertness came an extraordinary intellectual revival. He read widely in a blundering way, and he pondered unceasingly. It was characteristic of the man that, as soon as he left the paths of the prosaic, he should seek his supernatural in a very concrete form. He assumed that he was haunted by the Devil—the visible, personal Devil in whom our fathers believed. He waited hourly for the shape at his side to speak, but no words came. The Accuser of the Brethren in all but tangible form was his ever-present companion. He felt, he declared, the spirit of old evil entering subtly into his blood. He sold his soul many times over, and yet there was no possibility of resistance. It was a Visitation more undeserved than Job's, and a thousand-fold more awful.

For a week or more he was tortured with a

kind of religious mania.   When a man of a healthy,
secular mind finds himself adrift on the terrible
ocean of religious troubles, he is peculiarly helpless, for he has not the most rudimentary knowledge of the winds and tides.   It was useless to
call up his old carelessness ; he had suddenly
dropped into a new world where old proverbs
did not apply.   And all the while, mind you,
there was the shrieking terror of it—an intellect
all alive to the torture and the most unceasing
physical fear.   For a little he was on the near edge
of idiocy.

Then by accident it took a new form.   While
sitting with Sybil one day in the library, he began
listlessly to turn over the leaves of a book.   He
read a few pages, and found the hint of a story
like his own.   It was some French life of Justinian, one of the unscholarly productions of last
century, made up of stories from Procopius and
tags of Roman law.   Here was his own case
written down in black and white ; and the man
had been a king of kings !   This was a new comfort, and for a little—strange though it may seem
—he took a sort of pride in his affliction.   He
worshipped the great emperor and read every
scrap he could find on him, not excepting the
Pandects and the Digest.   He sent for the bust
in the dining-room, paying a fabulous price.   Then
he settled himself to study his imperial prototype,
and the study became an idolatry.   As I have
said, Ladlaw was a man of ordinary talents and
certainly of meagre imaginative power.   And yet

from the lies of the *Secret History* and the crudities of German legalists he had constructed a marvellous portrait of a man. Sitting there in the half-lit room, he drew the picture—the quiet, cold king with his inheritance of Dacian mysticism, holding the great world in fee, giving it law and religion, fighting its wars, building its churches, and yet all the while intent upon his own private work of making his peace with his soul. The churchman and warrior whom all the world worshipped, and yet one going through life with his lip quivering, the Watcher by the Threshold ever at his left side. Sometimes at night in the great Brazen Palace, warders heard the emperor walking in the dark corridors, alone and yet not alone; for once, when a servant entered with a lamp, he saw his master with a face as of another world, and something beside him which had no face or shape, but which he knew to be that hoary Evil which is older than the stars. Crazy nonsense! I had to rub my eyes to assure myself that I was not sleeping. No! There was my friend with his suffering face, and it was the library of More.

And then he spoke of Theodora—actress, harlot, *dévote*, empress. For him the lady was but another part of the uttermost horror, a form of the shapeless thing at his side. I felt myself falling under the fascination. I have no nerves and little imagination, but in a flash I seemed to realize something of that awful featureless face, crouching ever at a man's hand, till darkness and loneliness comes and it rises to its mastery. I shivered as

I looked at the man in the chair before me. Those dull eyes of his were looking upon things I could not see, and I saw their terror. I realized that it was grim earnest for him. Nonsense or no, some devilish fancy had usurped the place of sanity, and he was being slowly broken upon the wheel. And then, when his left hand twitched, I almost cried out. I had thought it comic before; now it seemed the last proof of tragedy.

He stopped, and I got up with loose knees and went to the window. Better the black night than the intangible horror within. I flung up the sash and looked out across the moor. There was no light, nothing but an inky darkness and the uncanny rustle of elder bushes. The sound chilled me, and I closed the window.

"The land is the old Manann," Ladlaw was saying. "We are beyond the pale here. Do you hear the wind?"

I forced myself back into sanity and looked at my watch. It was nearly one o'clock.

"What ghastly idiots we are!" I said. "I am off to bed."

Ladlaw looked at me helplessly. "For God's sake, don't leave me alone!" he moaned. "Get Sybil."

We went together back to the hall, while he kept the same feverish grip on my arm. Some one was sleeping in a chair by the hall fire, and to my distress I recognized my hostess. The poor child must have been sadly wearied. She came forward with her anxious face.

"I'm afraid Bob has kept you very late, Henry," she said. "I hope you will sleep well. Breakfast at nine, you know." And then I left them.

Over my bed there was a little picture, a reproduction of an Italian work of Christ and the Demoniac. Some impulse made me hold my candle up to it. The madman's face was torn with passion and suffering, and his eye had the pained furtive look which I had come to know. And by his left side there was a dim shape crouching.

I got into bed hastily, but not to sleep. I felt that my reason must be going. I had been pitchforked from our clear and cheerful modern life into the mists of old superstition. Old tragic stories of my Calvinist upbringing returned to haunt me. The man dwelt in by a devil was no new fancy; but I believed that Science had docketed and analysed and explained the Devil out of the world. I remembered my dabblings in the occult before I settled down to law—the story of Donisarius the monk of Padua, the unholy legend of the Face of Proserpina, the tales of *succubi* and *incubi*, the Leannain Sith and the Hidden Presence. But here was something stranger still. I had stumbled upon that very possession which fifteen hundred years ago had made the monks of New Rome tremble and cross themselves. Some devilish occult force, lingering through the ages, had come to life after a long sleep. God knows what earthly connection there was between the splendid Emperor of the World and my prosaic friend, or between the glittering shores of the Bosphorus and this moorland parish! But the land was the old Manann! The spirit may have lingered in the earth and air, a deadly legacy from Pict and Roman. I had felt the uncanniness of the place; I had augured ill of it from the first. And then in sheer disgust I rose and splashed my face with cold water.

I lay down again, laughing miserably at my credulity. That I, the sober and rational, should believe in this crazy fable, was too palpably absurd. I would steel my mind resolutely against such harebrained theories. It was a mere bodily ailment—liver out of order, weak heart, bad circulation, or something of that sort. At the worst it might be some affection of the brain to be treated by a specialist. I vowed to myself that next morning the best doctor in Edinburgh should be brought to More.

The worst of it was that my duty compelled me to stand my ground. I foresaw the few remaining weeks of my holiday blighted. I should be tied to this moorland prison, a sort of keeper and nurse in one, tormented by silly fancies. It was a charming prospect, and the thought of Glenaicill and the woodcock made me bitter against Ladlaw. But there was no way out of it. I might do Ladlaw good, and I could not have Sybil worn to death by his vagaries.

My ill-nature comforted me, and I forgot the

horror of the thing in its vexation. After that, I think I fell asleep and dozed uneasily till morning. When I awoke I was in a better frame of mind. The early sun had worked wonders with the moorland. The low hills stood out fresh-coloured and clear against the pale October sky, the elders sparkled with frost, the raw film of morn was rising from the little loch in tiny clouds. It was a cold rousing day, and I dressed in good spirits and went down to breakfast.

I found Ladlaw looking ruddy and well, very different from the broken man I remembered of the night before. We were alone, for Sybil was breakfasting in bed. I remarked on his ravenous appetite, and he smiled cheerily. He made two jokes during the meal, he laughed often, and I began to forget the events of the previous day. It seemed to me that I might still flee from More with a clear conscience. He had forgotten about his illness. When I touched distantly upon the matter he showed a blank face.

It might be that the affection had passed; on the other hand, it might return to him at the darkening—I had no means to decide. His manner was still a trifle *distrait* and peculiar, and I did not like the dullness in his eye. At any rate, I should spend the day in his company, and the evening would decide the question.

I proposed shooting, which he promptly vetoed. He was no good at walking, he said, and the birds were wild. This seriously limited the possible occupations. Fishing there was none, and hill

climbing was out of the question. He proposed
a game of billiards, and I pointed to the glory of
the morning. It would have been sacrilege to
waste such sunshine in knocking balls about.
Finally, we agreed to drive somewhere and have
lunch, and he ordered the dogcart.

In spite of all forebodings I enjoyed the day.
We drove in the opposite direction from the wood-
land parts, right away across the moor to the
coal country beyond. We lunched at the little
mining town of Borrowmuir, in a small and noisy
public-house. The roads made bad going, the
country was far from pretty, and yet the drive
did not bore me. Ladlaw talked incessantly,
talked as I had never heard man talk before.
There was something indescribable in all he said—
a different point of view, a lost groove of thought,
a kind of innocence and archaic shrewdness in one.
I can only give you a hint of it by saying that it
was like the mind of an early ancestor placed
suddenly among modern surroundings. It was
wise with a remote wisdom, and silly (now and
then) with a quite antique and distant silliness.

I will give you instances of both. He provided
me with a theory of certain early fortifications,
which must be true, which commends itself to the
mind with overwhelming conviction, and yet which
is so out of the way of common speculation that
no man could have guessed it. I do not propose
to set down the details, for I am working at it on
my own account. Again, he told me the story of
an old marriage custom, which till recently sur-

vived in this district—told it with full circumstantial detail and constant allusions to other
customs which he could not possibly have known
of. Now for the other side. He explained why
well-water is in winter warmer than a running
stream, and this was his explanation. At the
Antipodes our winter is summer ; consequently the
water of a well which comes through from the
other side of the earth must be warm in winter
and cold in summer, since in our summer it is
winter there. You perceive what this is. It is
no mere silliness, but a genuine effort of an early
mind which had just grasped the fact of the Antipodes, to use it in explanation.

Gradually I was forced to the belief that it was
not Ladlaw who was talking to me, but something
speaking through him, something at once wiser
and simpler. My old fear of the Devil began to
depart. This spirit, this exhalation, whatever it
was, was ingenuous in its way, at least in its daylight aspect. For a moment I had an idea that
it was a real reflex of Byzantine thought, and that
by cross-examining I might make marvellous discoveries. The ardour of the scholar began to rise
in me, and I asked a question about that much-
debated point, the legal status of the *apocrisiarii*.
To my vexation he gave no response. Clearly the
intelligence of this familiar had its limits.

It was about three in the afternoon, and we had
completed half of our homeward journey, when
signs of the old terror began to appear. I was
driving, and Ladlaw sat on my left. I noticed

him growing nervous and silent, shivering at the
flick of the whip, and turning half-way round towards me. Then he asked me to change places,
and I had the unpleasant work of driving from
the wrong side. After that I do not think he
spoke once till we arrived at More, but sat huddled
together with the driving rug almost up to his
chin—an eccentric figure of a man.

I foresaw another such night as the last, and I
confess my heart sank. I had no stomach for
more mysteries, and somehow with the approach
of twilight the confidence of the day departed.
The thing appeared in darker colours, and I could
have found it in my mind to turn coward. Sybil
alone deterred me. I could not bear to think of
her alone with this demented being. I remembered her shy timidity, her innocence. It was
monstrous that the poor thing should be called
on thus to fight alone with phantoms. So I braced
myself for another evening.

When we came to the house it was almost sunset. Ladlaw got out very carefully on the right
side, and for a second stood by the horse. The
sun was making our shadows long, and as I stood
beyond him, it seemed for a moment that his
shadow was double. It may have been mere fancy,
for I had not time to look twice. He was standing, as I have said, with his left side next the horse.
Suddenly the harmless elderly cob fell into a very
panic of fright, reared upright, and all but succeeded in killing its master. I was in time to
pluck Ladlaw from under its feet, but the beast

had become perfectly unmanageable, and we left a groom struggling to quiet it.

In the hall the butler gave me a telegram. It was from my clerk, summoning me back at once to an important consultation.

reported to be something of an orator, eagerly sought after by city congregations, but at present hiding his light under the bushel of Morebrig to allow him time to prepare some great theological work. Ladlaw had liked him in a half-amused and tolerant way, and he used to come sometimes to dine. His name was Bruce Oliphant, and he inhabited a dark manse at the outskirts of the village.

I had an hour before dinner, and I set out for Mr. Oliphant's dwelling. I remember the curious dull village street, without colour or life, drab women looking out of dingy doorways, and a solitary child playing in the red mud. The manse stood at the back of the usual elder thicket, a little place with small windows and a weather-stained front door. A gaunt old servant ushered me into Mr. Oliphant's study, where I found that young man smoking and reading a weekly paper. It was a room well stocked with books in the popular religious vein, and the Poets in gilt editions adorned his shelves. Mr. Oliphant greeted me with the nervous ease of one who would fain cultivate a good manner. The first sight of him sent my hopes down. He had a large calf-like face, mildly arrogant eyes, and a chin which fell sharply away beneath the eaves of his moustache. This was not one to do Ladlaw much good ; indeed I questioned if I could ever make him understand, for the man before me had an impenetrable air of omniscience.

"I have come to ask you a great favour on

behalf of the Ladlaws," said I. "You are the only other gentleman in the parish of More, and it is your duty to help your neighbours."

He bowed, with pleased eyes. "Anything," he said. "I'll be very glad."

"I am staying there just now, you know, and as it happens I must go back to town by the night train. I'll only be gone a day, but you know that Ladlaw is a melancholy beggar and gets low-spirited. Now I want you to go up and stay at the House for a couple of nights while I am away."

It was an odd request, and he stared at me. "Why, what's wrong with Mr. Ladlaw?" he asked. "I should never have called him melancholy. Now, his lady is different. She always looks a little pale. Did she send you to ask me?" Mr. Oliphant was a stickler for the usages of polite society.

I sat down in a chair and took one of his cigarettes. "Now, look here, Oliphant," I said. "You are a man of education and common sense, and I am going to do you the honour to tell you a story which I would not tell to a stupid man. A stupid man would laugh at me. I hope you will see the gravity of the thing."

I told him briefly the points in Ladlaw's case. His eyes grew very round as I went on, and when I finished he laughed nervously. He was clearly impressed; but he was too ignorant and un-imaginative to understand fully, and he had his credit as a representative of modern thought to support. "Oh, come now! You don't mean all that; I never heard the like of it. You can't expect me as a Christian man to believe in a Pagan spirit. I might as well believe in ghosts at once. What has the familiar of a heathen emperor to do with this parish?"

"Justinian was a Christian," I said.

He looked puzzled. "It's all preposterous. Meaning no disrespect to you, I must decline to believe it. My profession compels me to discourage such nonsense."

"So does mine," I said wearily. "Good Lord! man, do you think I came here to tell you a fairy tale? It's the most terrible earnest. Now I want you to give me an answer, for I have very little time."

He was still incredulous, and inclined to argue. "Do you know if Mr. Ladlaw has been—eh—a strictly temperate man?" he asked.

With this my patience departed. I got up to go, with rude thoughts on the stupidity of the clergy. But Mr. Oliphant was far from a refusal. He had no objection to exchange the barren comfort of the manse for the comparative luxury of the House, and he had no distrust of his power to enliven. As he accompanied me to the door he explained his position. "You see, if they really want me I will come. Tell Mrs. Ladlaw that I shall be delighted. Mrs. Ladlaw is a lady for whom I have a great respect."

"So have I," I said crossly. "Very well. A trap shall be sent for you after dinner. Good evening, Mr. Oliphant. It is a pleasure to have met you."

When I reached the House, I told Sybil of my arrangement. For the first time since my arrival she smiled. "It's very kind of him, but I am afraid he won't do much good. Bob will frighten him away."

"I fancy he won't. The man is strong in his self-confidence and remarkably dense. He'll probably exasperate Bob into sanity. In any case I'll be back by Friday morning."

As I drove away the trap arrived at the door, bringing Mr. Oliphant and his portmanteau.

*   *   *   *   *   *

The events of the next twenty-four hours, during which I was travelling in the Scotch express or transacting dreary business in my chambers, are known only from the narrative of the minister. He wrote it out some weeks after at my request, for I wished to have all the links in the tale. I propose to give the gist of it, as he wrote it, stripped of certain reflections on human life and an inscrutable Providence, with which he had garnished it.

Narrative of the Reverend Mr. Oliphant.

I arrived at the House of More at a quarter-past eight on the Wednesday evening. The family had dined early, as Mr. Grey was leaving for London, and when I arrived I was taken to the library, where I found Mr. Ladlaw. I had not seen him for some time, and thought him looking pale and a little haggard. He seemed glad to see me, and made me sit down in a chair on his left and draw it up close to him. I wondered at his manner, for though we had always been on good terms he had never admitted me to any close intimacy. But now he was more than amiable. He made me ring for toddy, and though he refused to taste it himself, he pressed the beverage on me. Then he gave me a large cigar, at which I trembled, and finally he said that we should play at picquet. I declined resolutely, for it is part of my conscience to refuse to join in any card games ; but he made no trouble, and indeed in a moment seemed to have forgotten his proposition.

The next thing he did startled my composure. For he asked abruptly, " Do you believe in a living personal Devil, Oliphant ? "

I was taken aback, but answered that to the best of my light I did not.

" And why not ? " he asked sharply.

I explained that it was an old, false, anthropo-morphic fiction, and that the modern belief was infinitely more impressive. I quoted the words of Dr. Rintoul, one of our Church leaders. I am sorry to say that Mr. Ladlaw's words were, " Dr. Rintoul be d—d ! "

" Who the deuce are you to change the belief of centuries ? " he cried. " Our forefathers believed in him. They saw him at evening slinking about the folds and peat-stacks, or wrapped up in a black gown standing in the pulpits of the Kirk. Are we wiser men than they?"

I answered that culture had undoubtedly advanced in our day.

Mr. Ladlaw replied with blasphemous words on modern culture. I had imagined him to be a gentleman of considerable refinement, and I knew he had taken a good degree at college. Consequently, I was disagreeably surprised at his new manner.

"You are nothing better than an ignorant parson"—these were his words—"and you haven't even the merits of your stupid profession. The old Scots ministers were Calvinists to the backbone, and they were strong men—strong men, do you hear?—and they left their mark upon the nation. But your new tea-meeting kind of parson, who has nothing but a smattering of bad German to commend him, is a nuisance to God and man. And they don't believe in the Devil! Well, he'll get them safe enough some day."

I implored him to remember my cloth, and curb his bad language.

"I say the Devil will get you all safe enough some day," he repeated.

I rose to retire in as dignified a manner as possible, but he was before me and closed the door. I began to be genuinely frightened.

"For God's sake, don't go!" he cried. "Don't leave me alone. Do sit down, Oliphant, like a good chap, and I promise to hold my tongue.

You don't know how horrible it is to be left alone."

I sat down again, though my composure was shaken. I remembered Mr. Grey's words about the strange sickness.

Then Mr. Ladlaw fell into an extraordinary moodiness. He sat huddled up in his chair, his face turned away from me, and for some time neither of us spoke a word. I thought that I had seriously offended him, and prepared to apologize, so I touched his left shoulder to attract his attention. Instantly he jumped to his feet, screaming, and turned on me a face of utter terror. I could do nothing but stare at him, and in a second he quieted down and returned to his seat.

Then he became partially sane, and murmured a sort of excuse. I thought that I would discover what truth lay in Mr. Grey's singular hypothesis. I did not ask him bluntly, as an ordinary man would have done, what was his malady, but tactfully, as I thought then, I led the conversation to demoniacal possession in the olden time, and quoted Pellinger's theory on the Scriptural cases. He answered with extraordinary vehemence, showing a childish credulity I little expected from an educated man.

"I see that you hold to the old interpretation," I said pleasantly. "Nowadays, we tend to find the solution in natural causes."

"Heavens, man!" he cried. "What do you mean by natural? You haven't the most rudi-

mentary knowledge of nature. Listen to me,
and I will tell you something."

And with this he began a long rambling account
of something which I could not understand. He
talked much about a name which sounded like
Canaan, and then he wandered to another subject and talked about Proserpina, whom I remembered from Mr. Matthew Arnold's poem.
I would have thought him trying to ridicule me,
if I had not seen his face, which was white and
drawn with pain ; and, again, I would have thought
him drunk, but for his well-known temperate
habits. By-and-by even my nerves, which are
very strong, began to suffer. I understood fragments of his talk, and the understanding did not
reassure me. It was poisonous nonsense, but
it had a terrible air of realism. He had a queer
habit of catching at his heart like a man with
the heart disease, and his eyes were like a mad
dog's I once saw, the pupils drawn to a pin-point
with fear. I could not bear it, so I tried to break
the spell. I offered, against my conscience, to play
a card game, but his face showed that he did not
understand me. I began to feel a sort of languor
of terror. I could hardly rise from my chair, and
when at last I got up the whole room seemed
haunted. I rushed to the bell and rang it violently,
and then tried to open the door. But he was before
me again, and gripped my arm so fiercely that I
cried out between the pain and my dread of him.

" Come back ! " he cried hoarsely. "Don't
leave me alone. For God's sake, Oliphant ! "

Just then the man-servant opened the door, and found the two of us standing like lunatics. I had the sense to save the situation, and I asked him to bring more coals for the fire. Then as soon as he turned to go, I stepped out of the open door before Mr. Ladlaw could prevent me.

The hall seemed empty, but to my surprise I found Mrs. Ladlaw sleeping in a chair by the fire. I did not like to waken her, but I was at my wits' end with fright. If I had known the way to the kitchen, I would have sought the servants' company. I ran down a passage, but it seemed to end in a blind wall, and in a great fear I turned and ran upstairs. But the upper lobbies seemed to be unlit, and I was turning back when I heard Ladlaw's voice behind me. It was muffled and queer, and the sound drove me into the darkness. When I turned a corner, to my relief I saw a lamp burning on a table and recognized my bedroom door. Here was sanctuary at last, and I ran in and shut it behind me.

My nerves were so shaken by the evening's performances that I found it impossible to get to sleep. I sat up the better part of the night by the fire, and smoked several cigarettes, which in ordinary circumstances I should never have dared to do in a strange bedroom. About four o'clock, I think, I dozed off in my chair, and awoke about nine, very stiff and cold, to find Ladlaw laughing at me in the doorway.

I was at first so confused that I did not remember what had scared me the night before. Then, as it came back to me, I was amazed at my host's appearance. He looked fresh and well, and in excellent spirits. He laughed immoderately when he found I had not gone to bed.

"You do look cheap," he said. "Breakfast's in half an hour. You will feel better when you have had a tub."

I bathed reluctantly, feeling ill and bitterly cold; but I was comforted by a good breakfast. Then I had an opportunity of talking to Mrs. Ladlaw. As I remembered her, she had been full of gaiety, and even, I thought, a little frivolous; but now she was so pale and silent that I pitied her sincerely. I began to feel an intense dislike of her husband, partly for the fright he had given me the night before, and partly for the effect his silliness seemed to be having on his wife. The day was a fine one, but after breakfast he showed no intention of going out. I expected to be asked to shoot, a sport which I sometimes try; but he never spoke of it, and insisted on my coming to the billiard-room. As we were leaving the table Mrs. Ladlaw touched my arm, and asked me in a low tone if I would promise to stay all day with her husband. "I want to go down to Morefoot," she said, "and you know he cannot be left alone." I promised willingly, for in the daylight Mr. Ladlaw had no terrors for me. I thought that Mrs. Ladlaw looked relieved. Poor thing! she badly needed a respite.

We hung aimlessly about the place till lunch, playing a few games of billiards, and in the intervals looking at stables and harness-rooms and the now barren gardens. At lunch Mrs. Ladlaw appeared, but immediately after I heard wheels on the gravel and knew that she had gone to More-foot. Then I began to feel nervous again. I was the only responsible person left in the place, and Mr. Ladlaw might at any moment relapse into craziness. I watched his moods anxiously, and talked all the nonsense I knew to keep him in good humour. I told him stories, I talked wildly of sport, I made ridiculous jokes at which I felt myself blushing. At first he seemed amused, but soon I felt that my words were falling on deaf ears. He himself began to talk, violently, in-cessantly, and, I may say, brilliantly. If my memory had been better and my balance less upset, I might have made my reputation, though it would have been a reputation perhaps that a minister of the Gospel might well look askance at. I could have written a terrible romance from that man's babbling. Nay, I could have done more : I could have composed a new philosophy which would have cast Nietzsche in the shade for ever. I do not wish to exaggerate, but I have never been so impressed with a sense of a crazy intellectual acumen. This Mr. Ladlaw, whom I had known as a good landlord and a respectable country gentleman, now appeared as a kind of horrible genius, a brilliant and malignant satyr. I was shocked and confounded, and at the same time filled with admiration. I remember that we passed through the dining-room, where there was a great marble bust of a Roman emperor, an old discoloured thing, but wonderful in its way. Mr. Ladlaw stopped before it and pointed out its merits. The thing seemed simple enough, and yet after the description I fled from it as if it had been a devil. He followed me, still talking, and we found ourselves in the library.

I remember that I suggested tea, but he scarcely heeded me. The darkness was falling, Mrs. Ladlaw had not returned, and I felt horribly uncomfortable. I tried to draw him away from the room which I feared, but he made no sign of understanding. I perceived that the malady of the last night was returning. I hated that library, with its low fire, its ghastly white books, and its dreary outlook. I picked up one volume, and it was lettered on the back *Sancti Adelberti Certamina.* I dropped it, only to feel Mr. Ladlaw clutching my right arm and dragging me to one of those horrible arm-chairs.

"The night is coming on, the old Nox Atra that the monks dreaded. Promise me that you won't go away."

I promised feebly, and prayed for Mrs. Ladlaw's return. I suggested that the lamps should be lit. He rose and tried to light the hanging central one, and I noticed how his hands trembled. His awkwardness upset the thing, and it fell with a crash on the floor. He jumped back with a curious scream like an animal.

I was so miserably scared that I had not the heart to do the work for him, so we sat on in the darkness. Any sound from the out-of-doors would have comforted me, but the whole world was as silent as death. I felt that a little more would drive me mad, and the thought roused me to make a final effort after safety. In spite of all my promises I must get away. A man's first duty is to himself, and the hour had come for me. I thought with longing of my little bare manse and my solemn housekeeper. And yet how was I to escape, for this man was the stronger, and he would never let me go.

I begged him to come into the hall, but he refused. Then I became very cunning. I suggested that we should go to the door and receive Mrs. Ladlaw. He did not know that she had gone, and the news made him so nervous that he accepted my proposal. He caught my arm as before, and, leaning heavily upon me, went into the hall. There was no one about, and the fire had died down ; but at the far end there was a pale glimmer from the glass door. We opened it and stood on the top step, looking over the dark lawns. Now was the time for an effort for freedom. If I could only get rid of his hand I might escape across the fields. I believed him to be too weak on his legs to follow me, and in any case I was a respectable runner. Out of doors he seemed less formidable : it was only in that haunted room that I shuddered.

I took the only way of escape which presented itself. There was a flowering shrub in a pot on the top of the parapet. I caught this with my elbow and knocked it over, so that it broke with a clatter on the stone. As I expected, he screamed and jumped aside, letting go my arm for one instant. The next I was down the steps and running hard across the lawns to the park beyond.

For a little I heard him stumbling after me, breathing heavily and with short broken cries. I ran with the speed of fear, for till I was within my own doors I could feel no security. Once I turned, and there he was, a field behind me, running with his head down like a blind dog. I skirted the village, broke through the little fir plantation, and came out on the highway. I saw the light from Jean's little window, and it was like a beacon of hope. In a few minutes I was at the door, and my servant stared as I rushed in, without hat or overcoat, and wet with perspiration. I insisted on barring the doors, and bolting and shuttering every window. Then I had the unusual luxury of a fire in my bedroom, and there I supped, and sat till I fell asleep.

End of Mr. Oliphant's Statement.

CHAPTER III

EVENTS ON THE UPLANDS

I RETURNED from town by the night express, which landed me at Borrowmuir about seven on the Friday morning. To my surprise there was no dogcart to meet me, as had been arranged, and I was compelled to hire from the inn. The omission filled me with forebodings. Things must have gone badly at More in my absence, or the careful Sybil would never have forgotten. I grudged the time occupied in that weary drive. The horse seemed intolerably slow, the roads unaccountably steep. It was a sharp morning, with haze on the fields and promise of bright sunshine at midday ; but, tired as I was with my two days' journey, I was in the humour to see little good in my case. I was thankful when we drew up at the house door, and, cold and stiff, I hobbled up the steps.

The door was open, and I entered. The hall was empty, there was no sign of any servant, and all the doors were wide to the wall. I tried one room after another without success. Then I made my voice heard in that place. I shouted

for Ladlaw, and then I shouted for Sybil. There
came no answer, and in despair I rushed to the
kitchen wing. There I found a cluster of frightened
maids, and by dint of much questioning learned
the truth.

Ladlaw, it seemed, had disappeared from the
house about a quarter-past six on the previous
night. The minister had decamped and found
sanctuary in the manse; but there was no trace
of the other. Sybil had gone to Morefoot in the
afternoon, and, returning about half-past six,
found her husband gone. She had been dis-
tracted with anxiety, had gone to the manse,
where she found Mr. Oliphant in a state of nervous
collapse and quite unable to make any coherent
statement, and had then roused some of the neigh-
bouring shepherds and organized a search party.
They had searched all night, but so far no word
had come of the result. Meanwhile, Sybil, utterly
wearied and a little hysterical, was in bed, sleeping, for her anxiety of the past week had cul-
minated in a sort of deep languor, which in the
circumstances was the best thing that could have
happened. There was no question of wakening
her; but, as I snatched a hurried breakfast, it
seemed to me that I must at once follow the search.
They were to meet in the morning at a farm called
Mossrigging, beneath a hill of the same name,
and if I went there I might get word of them. In
the meantime I must interview Mr. Oliphant.

I found him in bed, unshaven, and very hollow
about the eyes. He told me a lame story, and

indeed his fright was so palpable that I had not the heart to blame him. But I insisted that he should get up and come with me, for every man would be needed to search those mossy uplands. I was dog-tired, sleepy, and irritable, and yet I must go : why should not this man, who had had his night's rest ?

He made some feeble objection ; but he had a conscience of his own and rose obediently. We set out to the nearest part of the moor, he in his clergyman's garb, and I in a dark suit and a bowler ; and I remember thinking how oddly unsuited was our dress for this stalking game. I was wretchedly anxious, for I liked Ladlaw, and God alone knew where he might have got to in the night. There were deep bogs and ugly old pit-shafts on the moor, and there were ravines with sheer red sides. At any moment we might find tragedy, and I dreaded the report of the searchers at Mossrigging.

When we left the road, we followed an old cart track up a shallow glen, where stood some curious old stone chimneys, which had been built by a speculator who hoped to make a fortune from peat. The sun was beginning to break through the haze, and miles of low moorland were disclosed to left and right. But the hills in front were still cloudy, and we were close on the cottage before we knew its whereabouts. It stood high in a crinkle of hill, with a wide prospect north and east to the sea, and as I turned I saw Morebrig smoking clear in the autumn light,

and the chimneys of the House above the fir
trees.   Out on the waters three ships were sailing
like toy boats, a reminder of the bustling modern
life beyond this antique place of horrors.

The house was full of men, devouring their
morning porridge.   They were shepherds of the
neighbourhood, and two boys from the village,
as well as John Ker, the head keeper from More.
One man, Robert Tod by name, answered my un-
spoken question.   " We havena gotten him, but
we've gotten his whereabouts.   We got a glisk
o' him about six this mornin' on the back side
o' the Lowe Moss.   I kent him fine by the way
he ran.   Lord, but he was souple !   Nane o' us
could come within a hunner yairds o' him.   We'll
hae to wyse him gently, sir, and some o' us 'll
hae to tak a lang cast round the hill."

I had no ambition to " tak a lang cast round
the hill " ; but these men had been abroad all
night, and I and the minister must undertake
the duty.   Tod agreed to come with us, and the
shaggy silent men of the party expounded the
plan of campaign.   The Lowe Moss was impassable on one side, on another bounded by a steep
hill-shoulder, and on the others by two narrow
glens.   They would watch the glens ; we three
should make a circuit and come back over the hill,
driving the fugitive before us.   Once enclosed
between the moss and our three parties, he should
be an easy capture.   I implored them to go to
work gently, for I feared that he might be driven
into the bog.   They shook their heads and

laughed : it was all a kind of crazy sport to them, and their one idea was to carry out their orders.

I confess I was desperately tired before we had forded the upper waters of the More, crossed the Redscaurhead, and looked over the green pasture-lands to the south. It was a most curious sight ; for whereas one side of the range was rough and mossy and hideous with red scaurs, the other was a gentle slope with sweet hill grass and bright shallow waters. It was a new country where the old curse could not reign, and an idea took possession of me that if once Ladlaw came into the place he would be healed of his malady. The air seemed clearer, the sky softer, the whole world simple and clean. We fetched a circuit down one of the little streams till we came to the back of the hill which on its face is called Mossrigging. I was abominably tired, but in better spirits. As for the minister, he groaned occasionally, but never spoke a word.

At the foot we separated to the distance of half a mile, and began the ascent. So far there was no sign of our man. Tod was on the far east, I was in the centre, and Mr. Oliphant took the west. I cannot profess to remember exactly all the incidents of that climb. I was too stupid with sleep and exertion, and the little distant figures of my companions danced in a kind of haze. The ascent was simple—short grass, varied by short heather, with at wide intervals a patch of shingle. The shepherd walked with an easy swing, the minister stumbled and groaned, while

I, in sheer bravado and irritation at my weakness, kept up a kind of despairing trot. The Devil and Ladlaw combined might confront me, but I was too tired to care. Indeed, in a little I had forgotten all about the purpose of our quest.

Then, quite suddenly, almost at the summit, in a little hollow of the ridge, I saw our man. He was sitting on the ground, directly in the minister's line, and his head was sunk on his breast. I remember being taken with a horrid thought that he was dead, and quickened my trot to a run. Meanwhile the minister was approaching very near, but apparently quite unconscious of his presence. His eyes were in the ends of the earth, and he ambled along with no purpose in the world.

What happened rests mainly on my authority; but Robert Tod, shepherd in Nether Mossrigging, is ready to swear to the essentials. Mr. Oliphant stumbled on into the hollow till he was within ten yards of the sitting figure. Ladlaw never moved; but the subtle influence which tells of human presence came suddenly upon the minister's senses, for he lifted his eyes and started. The man was still scared to death, and he naturally turned to run away, when something happened which I cannot well explain. Ladlaw was still sitting with his head on his breast, and yet it was clear to my mind that Ladlaw had somehow risen and was struggling with the minister. I could see the man's wrists strained and twisted as if in a death-grapple, and his white face reddening with exertion. He seemed to be held round the middle, for his feet tottered several times, and once he lurched to the left side, so that I thought he was thrown. And yet he was only battling with the air, for there was Ladlaw sitting quietly some yards from him.

And then suddenly the contest seemed to cease. Mr. Oliphant ran straight past the sitting man and over the brow of the hill. Surprise had held Tod and myself motionless. Now the spell was broken, and from our several places we ran towards Ladlaw. I heard the shepherd's loud voice crying, "Look at Oliphant! Oliphant's no wise!" and I thought I heard a note of sardonic mirth. In any case, it was the minister he was after, for a moment later he disappeared down the farther slope.

Mr. Oliphant might go where he pleased, but my business was with my friend. I caught Ladlaw by the shoulder and shook him fiercely. Then I pulled him to his feet, let him go, and he rolled over. The sight was so comic that I went into a fit of nervous laughter; but the shock seemed to have restored his wits, for he opened sleepy eyes and regarded me solemnly. I do not propose to analyse my reasons, but I was conscious that it was the old Ladlaw who was looking at me. I knew he was healed of his malady, but how I knew it I do not know. He stuck both fists into his eyes like a sleepy child. Then he yawned, and looked down ruefully at soaked, soiled, and ragged clothing. Then he looked reproachfully at me.

"What's up?" he asked. "Stop that hideous row and tell me what has happened. Have I had an accident?"

Then I spoke cunningly. "Nothing much. A little bit of a fall, but you'll be all right soon. Why, you look better already." And again I went into a fit of laughter.

He grew wholesomely cross. "Oh, don't be a confounded jackass!" he cried. "I feel as if I hadn't slept for a week, and I'm hungry and thirsty."

He swallowed the contents of my flask, and wolfed my sandwiches in a disgusting way. Then he proposed that we should go home. "I'm tired, and I'm sick of shooting for the day. By-the-by, where's my gun?"

"Broken," I said, "broken in the fall. The keeper is going to look after it." And with the aid of my arm he began with feeble steps his homeward journey.

* * * * * *

The minister—this is the tale of Robert Tod and his colleagues—descended the precipitous part of Mossrigging like a thing inspired. Tod, labouring heavily in his wake, declared that he went down the hillside like a loose stone, slipping, stumbling, yet never altogether losing his feet, and clearing dangers solely by the grace of God. As he went, said the men, he made clutches at the air, and his face was the face of one distraught. They ran together from their different places to intercept him on the edge of the bog, for at first

they thought he was Ladlaw. When they saw
their mistake they did not stop, for Tod was making
frantic signals for pursuit. John Ker, the More
keeper, was nearest, and he declared afterwards
that he never approached a business so unwill-
ingly. " I wad hae grippet a wild stot or a daft
staig suner nor yon man," he said. But the
business was too public for sheer cowardice. John
assaulted him on the left flank while the other
attacked in front, and John was bowled over like
a ninepin. It was not the minister, he said, but
something else, something with an arm two yards
long, which flew out like a steam hammer. But
the others were more fortunate. One caught
Mr. Oliphant's right arm, another hung on to the
flaps of his coat, while a third tripped him up
gallantly, till the whole body of them rolled on
the ground. Then ensued an indescribable fray.
Tod got a black eye from some unknown source,
and one of the boys lost several front teeth. Howls
of rage filled the moorland air, and all the while,
they declared, the minister was praying with
an unction which was never heard in the kirk.
" Lord, give me peace ! " he cried. " Lord, take
the thing away ! " and then again, " Get thee
behind me, Satan ! "

The end came very suddenly, for the company
rolled into the bog. The minister, being lowest,
saved the others, but he floundered in the green
slime up to his middle. The accident seemed
to inspire sobriety. He ceased his prayers, his
face lost its horror, and took on a common human

fear. Then Tod and his friends laboured heroic-
ally to rescue him, and all the while, they declared, something was pommelling them and
bruising them, and they showed for long black
marks on their bodies. Slowly they raised Mr.
Oliphant from the slough, and on a bridge of
coats he crept back to solid land.

And then that happened which was the crown
ing marvel of the business. It was a still sharp
day ; but suddenly there came a wind, hot and
harsh, and like nothing they had ever known.
It stung them like nettles, played for a moment
in their midst, and then in a kind of visible cloud
passed away from them over the bog in the direction of the Red Loch. And with the wind went
the Thing which had so long played havoc in the
place ; and the men were left with an unkempt
figure, coated with slime and shivering with fright,
but once more the sane and prosaic Mr. Oliphant,
the minister of the parish of More.

*   *   *   *   *   *

We got Ladlaw and the minister back to the
house with much trouble, for both were weak on
their legs, and one was still in a pitiable fright.
The two kept eyeing each other, one with a sort
of disgusted amusement, the other with a wondering fear. The shepherds were mystified ; but
they were matter-of-fact beings, who, having
fulfilled their orders, gave no more thought to
the business. The wounded nursed their bruises
and swore cheerfully, and the boy with the broken
teeth whistled his complaints. A good dinner

restored them to humour, and the last I saw was Ker and Tod going over the Odyssey of their adventures to a circle of critical spectators.

When Ladlaw and the minister had washed and fed, and sat smoking in the library, I went to talk to Sybil. I have often wondered how much she understood. At any rate she took my word that the trouble had passed, and in a fit of tears thanked me for my labours. Then she said she would go to her husband, and I led her to the library, where the two heroes were smoking the pipe of peace.

Ladlaw greeted her cheerily as if nothing had happened. " I feel a bit shaken," he said, " but I'll be all right after a night's rest. You needn't be nervous, Sib. By-the-by, Harry, where's that gun ? "

Then he wandered round the room, casting an unfriendly eye on his new acquisitions. " Look here ! Somebody has been playing the fool in this place. I can't see a single Badminton, and where did this stuff come from ? " And he tapped a row of books in old vellum. " I never remember the things before. St. Adelbert ! Who on earth was he ? Why, any one who came in suddenly and did not know me might think I was a minor poet. I wish you'd tell Harrison to clear all this truck away."

The minister sat by the fire and said nothing. The marvellous had intruded upon his easy life and spoiled the balance. I was sorry for the man, as I thanked him in a low tone and asked how he felt.

The words came from between chattering teeth.

" I am getting b-better," he said, " but I have had a terrible sh-shock.—I am a Christian man and I have been tempted.   I thought we lived in a progressive age, but now I know that we d-d-don't. And I am going to write to Dr. Rintoul."

1900.

IV

THE OUTGOING OF THE TIDE

THE OUTGOING OF THE TIDE *

> "Between the hours of twelve and one, even at the
> turning of the tide."

MEN come from distant parts to admire the
tides of Solloway, which race in at flood and
retreat at ebb with a greater speed than a horse
can follow. But nowhere are there queerer waters
than in our own parish of Caulds at the place
called the Sker Bay, where between two horns of
land a shallow estuary receives the stream of the
Sker. I never daunder by its shores, and see the
waters hurrying like messengers from the great
deep, without solemn thoughts and a memory of
Scripture words on the terror of the sea. The
vast Atlantic may be fearful in its wrath, but with
us it is no clean open rage, but the deceit of the
creature, the unholy ways of quicksands when the
waters are gone, and their stealthy return like a
thief in the night watches. But in the times of
which I write there were more awful fears than
any from the violence of nature. It was before
the day of my ministry in Caulds, for then I was

---

* From the unpublished Remains of the Reverend John Den-
nistoun, sometime minister of the Gospel in the parish of Caulds,
and author of *Satan's Artifices against the Elect.*

183

a bit callant in short clothes in my native parish
of Lesmahagow ; but the worthy Doctor Chrystal,
who had charge of spiritual things, has told me
often of the power of Satan and his emissaries in
that lonely place. It was the day of warlocks
and apparitions, now happily driven out by the
zeal of the General Assembly. Witches pursued
their wanchancy calling, bairns were spirited away,
young lassies selled their souls to the evil one, and
the Accuser of the Brethren in the shape of a
black tyke was seen about cottage doors in the
gloaming. Many and earnest were the prayers of
good Doctor Chrystal, but the evil thing, in spite
of his wrestling, grew and flourished in his midst.
The parish stank of idolatry, abominable rites
were practised in secret, and in all the bounds
there was no one had a more evil name for this
black traffic than one Alison Sempill, who bode
at the Skerburnfoot.

The cottage stood nigh the burn in a little garden
with lilyoaks and grosart bushes lining the pathway. The Sker ran by in a linn among hollins,
and the noise of its waters was ever about the
place. The highroad on the other side was fre-
quented by few, for a nearer-hand way to the
west had been made through the Lowe Moss.
Sometimes a herd from the hills would pass by
with sheep, sometimes a tinkler or a wandering
merchant, and once in a long while the laird of
Heriotside on his grey horse riding to Gledsmuir.
And they who passed would see Alison hirpling in
her garden, speaking to herself like the ill wife she

feet from the snares of evil-doers which had been
spread around her youth. She had been told unholy charms like the seven south streams and the
nine rowan berries, and it was noted when she
went first to the catechising that she prayed " Our
Father which wert in heaven," the prayer which
the ill wife Alison had taught her, meaning by it
Lucifer, who had been in heaven and had been
cast out therefrom. But when she had come to
years of discretion she had freely chosen the better
part, and evil had ever been repelled from her
soul like Gled water from the stones of Gled brig.
Now she was in a rapture of holy content. The
drucken bell—for the ungodly fashion lingered in
Caulds—was ringing in her ears as she left the
village, but to her it was but a kirk bell and a
goodly sound. As she went through the woods
where the primroses and the whitethorn were
blossoming, the place seemed as the land of Elam,
wherein there were twelve wells and threescore
and ten palm trees. And then, as it might be,
another thought came into her head, for it is
ordained that frail mortality cannot long continue
in holy joy. In the kirk she had been only the
bride of Christ ; but as she came through the
wood, with the birds lilting and the winds of the
world blowing, she had mind of another lover.

For this lass, though so cold to men, had not
escaped the common fate. It seemed that the
young Heriotside, riding by one day, stopped to
speir something or other, and got a glisk of Ailie's
face, which caught his fancy. He passed the road

again many times, and then he would meet her
in the gloaming or of a morning in the field as
she went to fetch the kye. "Blue are the hills
that are far away" is an owercome in the countryside, and while at first on his side it may have
been but a young man's fancy, to her he was like
the god Apollo descending from the skies. He
was good to look on, brawly dressed, and with a
tongue in his head that would have wiled the bird
from the tree. Moreover, he was of gentle kin,
and she was a poor lass biding in a cot-house with
an ill-reputed mother. It seems that in time the
young man, who had begun the affair with no
good intentions, fell honestly in love, while she
went singing about the doors as innocent as a
bairn, thinking of him when her thoughts were
not on higher things. So it came about that long
ere Ailie reached home it was on young Heriotside that her mind dwelt, and it was the love of
him that made her eyes glow and her cheeks
redden.

Now it chanced that at that very hour her
master had been with Alison, and the pair of them
were preparing a deadly pit. Let no man say that
the devil is not a cruel tyrant. He may give his
folk some scrapings of unhallowed pleasure; but
he will exact tithes, yea of anise and cummin, in
return, and there is aye the reckoning to pay at
the hinder end. It seems that now he was driving
Alison hard. She had been remiss of late, fewer
souls sent to hell, less zeal in quenching the Spirit,
and above all the crowning offence that her bairn

had communicated in Christ's kirk. She had waited overlong, and now it was like that Ailie would escape her toils. I have no skill of fancy to tell of that dark collogue, but the upshot was that Alison swore by her lost soul and the pride of sin to bring the lass into thrall to her master. The fiend had bare departed when Ailie came over the threshold to find the auld carline glunching by the fire.

It was plain she was in the worst of tempers. She flyted on the lass till the poor thing's cheek paled. "There you gang," she cried, "troking wi' thae wearifu' Pharisees o' Caulds, whae daurna darken your mither's door. A bonnie dutiful child, quotha! Wumman, hae ye nae pride?— no even the mense o' a tinkler lass?" And then she changed her voice, and would be as soft as honey. "My puir wee Ailie! was I thrawn till ye? Never mind, my bonnie. You and me are a' that's left, and we maunna be ill to ither." And then the two had their dinner, and all the while the auld wife was crooning over the lass. "We maun 'gree weel," she says, "for we're like to be our lee-lane for the rest o' our days. They tell me Heriotside is seeking Joan o' the Croft, and they're sune to be cried in Gledsmuir kirk."

It was the first the lass had heard of it, and you may fancy she was struck dumb. And so with one thing and other the auld witch raised the fiends of jealousy in that innocent heart. She would cry out that Heriotside was an ill-doing wastrel, and had no business to come and flatter

honest lassies. And then she would speak of
his gentle birth and his leddy mother, and say
it was indeed presumption to hope that so great
a gentleman could mean all that he said. Before
long Ailie was silent and white, while her mother
rhymed on about men and their ways. And then
she could thole it no longer, but must go out and
walk by the burn to cool her hot brow and calm
her thoughts, while the witch indoors laughed
to herself at her devices.

For days Ailie had an absent eye and a sad
face, and it so fell out that in all that time young
Heriotside, who had scarce missed a day, was
laid up with a broken arm and never came near
her. So in a week's time she was beginning to
hearken to her mother when she spoke of incan-
tations and charms for restoring love. She kenned
it was sin; but though not seven days syne she
had sat at the Lord's table, so strong is love in
a young heart that she was on the very brink of
it. But the grace of God was stronger than her
weak will. She would have none of her mother's
runes and philters, though her soul cried out for
them. Always when she was most disposed to
listen some merciful power stayed her consent.
Alison grew thrawner as the hours passed. She
kenned of Heriotside's broken arm, and she feared
that any day he might recover and put her strata-
gems to shame. And then it seems that she
collogued with her master and heard word of a
subtler device. For it was approaching that
uncanny time of year, the festival of Beltane,

when the auld pagans were wont to sacrifice to
their god Baal. In this season warlocks and
carlines have a special dispensation to do evil,
and Alison waited on its coming with graceless
joy. As it happened, the tides in the Sker Bay
ebbed at this time between the hours of twelve
and one, and, as I have said, this was the hour
above all others when the powers of darkness
were most potent. Would the lass but consent
to go abroad in the unhallowed place at this awful
season and hour of the night, she was as firmly
handfasted to the devil as if she had signed a
bond with her own blood. For there, it seemed,
the forces of good fled far away, the world for one
hour was given over to its ancient prince, and the
man or woman who willingly sought the spot
was his bond-servant for ever. There are deadly
sins from which God's people may recover. A
man may even communicate unworthily, and yet,
so be it he sin not against the Holy Ghost, he may
find forgiveness. But it seems that for this Beltane sin there could be no pardon, and I can
testify from my own knowledge that they who once
committed it became lost souls from that day.
James Deuchar, once a promising professor, fell
thus out of sinful bravery and died blaspheming;
and of Kate Mallison, who went the same road,
no man can tell. Here, indeed, was the witch-
wife's chance, and she was the more eager, for her
master had warned her that this was her last
chance. Either Ailie's soul would be his, or her
auld wrinkled body and black heart would be

(2,257)   13

flung from this pleasant world to their appor-
tioned place.

Some days later it happened that young Heriotside was stepping home over the Lang Muir about
ten at night—it being his first jaunt from home
since his arm had mended. He had been to the
supper of the Forest Club at the Cross Keys in
Gledsmuir, a clamjamfry of wild young blades
who passed the wine and played at cartes once
a fortnight. It seems he had drunk well, so that
the world ran round about and he was in the best
of tempers. The moon came down and bowed
to him, and he took off his hat to it. For every
step he travelled miles, so that in a little he was
beyond Scotland altogether and pacing the Ara-
bian desert. He thought he was the Pope of
Rome, so he held out his foot to be kissed, and rolled
twenty yards to the bottom of a small brae. Syne
he was the King of France, and fought hard with
a whin-bush till he had banged it to pieces. After
that nothing would content him but he must
be a bogle, for he found his head dunting on the
stars and his legs were knocking the hills together.
He thought of the mischief he was doing to the
auld earth, and sat down and cried at his wicked-
ness. Then he went on, and maybe the steep
road to the Moss Rig helped him, for he began
to get soberer and ken his whereabouts.

On a sudden he was aware of a man linking
along at his side. He cried " A fine night," and
the man replied. Syne, being merry from his
cups, he tried to slap him on the back. The

next he kenned he was rolling on the grass, for
his hand had gone clean through the body and
found nothing but air.

His head was so thick with wine that he found
nothing droll in this. "Faith, friend," he says,
"that was a nasty fall for a fellow that has supped
weel. Where might your road be gaun to?"

"To the World's End," said the man; "but
I stop at the Skerburnfoot."

"Bide the night at Heriotside," says he. "It's
a thought out of your way, but it's a comfortable bit."

"There's mair comfort at the Skerburnfoot,"
said the dark man.

Now the mention of the Skerburnfoot brought
back to him only the thought of Ailie and not of
the witch-wife, her mother. So he jaloused no
ill, for at the best he was slow in the uptake.

The two of them went on together for a while,
Heriotside's fool head filled with the thought of
the lass. Then the dark man broke silence.
"Ye're thinkin' o' the maid Ailie Sempill," says
he.

"How ken ye that?" asked Heriotside.

"It is my business to read the herts o' men,"
said the other.

"And who may ye be?" said Heriotside,
growing eerie.

"Just an auld packman," said he—"nae name
ye wad ken, but kin to mony gentle houses."

"And what about Ailie, you that ken sae
muckle?" asked the young man.

" Naething," was the answer—" naething that concerns you, for ye'll never get the lass."

" By God, and I will ! " says Heriotside, for he was a profane swearer.

" That's the wrong name to seek her in, any-way," said the man.

At this the young laird struck a great blow at him with his stick, but found nothing to resist him but the hill wind.

When they had gone on a bit the dark man spoke again. " The lassie is thirled to holy things," says he. " She has nae care for flesh and blood, only for devout contemplation."

" She loves me," says Heriotside.

" Not you," says the other, " but a shadow in your stead."

At this the young man's heart began to tremble, for it seemed that there was truth in what his companion said, and he was ower drunk to think gravely.

" I kenna whatna man ye are," he says, " but ye have the skill of lassies' hearts. Tell me truly, is there no way to win her to common love ? "

" One way there is," said the man, " and for our friendship's sake I will tell it you. If ye can ever tryst wi' her on Beltane's Eve on the Sker sands, at the green link o' the burn where the sands begin, on the ebb o' the tide when the mid-night is bye but afore cockcrow, she'll be yours, body and soul, for this world and for ever."

And then it appeared to the young man that he was walking his lone up the grass walk of Heriot-

side, with the house close by him. He thought
no more of the stranger he had met, but the word
stuck in his heart.

It seems that about this very time Alison was
telling the same tale to poor Ailie. She cast up
to her every idle gossip she could think of. " It's
Joan o' the Croft," was aye her owercome, and
she would threep that they were to be cried in
kirk on the first Sabbath of May. And then
she would rhyme on about the black cruelty of
it, and cry down curses on the lover, so that her
daughter's heart grew cauld with fear. It is
terrible to think of the power of the world even in
a redeemed soul. Here was a maid who had
drunk of the well of grace and tasted of God's
mercies, and yet there were moments when she
was ready to renounce her hope. At those awful
seasons God seemed far off and the world very
nigh, and to sell her soul for love looked a fair
bargain. At other times she would resist the
devil and comfort herself with prayer ; but aye
when she woke there was the sore heart, and
when she went to sleep there were the weary eyes.
There was no comfort in the goodliness of spring
or the bright sunshine weather, and she who had
been wont to go about the doors lightfoot and
blithe was now as dowie as a widow woman.

And then one afternoon in the hinder end of
April came young Heriotside riding to the Skerburnfoot. His arm was healed, he had got him
a fine new suit of green, and his horse was a mettle
beast that well set off his figure. Ailie was stand-

ing by the doorstep as he came down the road,
and her heart stood still with joy. But a second
thought gave her anguish. This man, so gallant
and braw, would never be for her; doubtless the
fine suit and the capering horse were for Joan o'
the Croft's pleasure. And he in turn, when he
remarked her wan cheek and dowie eyes, had mind
of what the dark man said on the muir, and saw
in her a maid sworn to no mortal love. Yet the
passion for her had grown fiercer than ever, and
he swore to himself that he would win her back
from her phantasies. She, one may believe, was
ready enough to listen. As she walked with
him by the Sker water his words were like music
to her ears, and Alison within-doors laughed to
herself and saw her devices prosper.

He spoke to her of love and his own heart,
and the girl hearkened gladly. Syne he rebuked
her coldness and cast scorn upon her piety, and
so far was she beguiled that she had no answer.
Then from one thing and another he spoke of
some true token of their love. He said he was
jealous, and craved a token to ease his care. "It's
but a small thing I ask," says he; "but it will
make me a happy man, and nothing ever shall
come atween us. Tryst wi' me for Beltane's
Eve on the Sker sands, at the green link o' the
burn where the sands begin, on the ebb o' the
tide when midnight is bye but afore cockcrow.
For," said he, "that was our forbears' tryst for
true lovers, and wherefore no for you and me?"

The lassie had grace given her to refuse, but

with a woeful heart, and Heriotside rode off in
black discontent, leaving poor Ailie to sigh her
lone. He came back the next day and the next,
but aye he got the same answer. A season of
great doubt fell upon her soul. She had no clearness in her hope, nor any sense of God's promises.
The Scriptures were an idle tale to her, prayer
brought her no refreshment, and she was con-
victed in her conscience of the unpardonable
sin. Had she been less full of pride she would
have taken her troubles to good Doctor Chrystal
and got comfort ; but her grief made her silent
and timorous, and she found no help anywhere.
Her mother was ever at her side, seeking with
coaxings and evil advice to drive her to the irrevocable step. And all the while there was her
love for the man riving in her bosom and giving
her no ease by night or day. She believed she
had driven him away and repented her denial.
Only her pride held her back from going to Heriotside and seeking him herself. She watched the
road hourly for a sight of his face, and when the
darkness fell she would sit in a corner brooding
over her sorrows.

At last he came, speiring the old question.
He sought the same tryst, but now he had a further tale. It seemed he was eager to get her
away from the Skerburnside and auld Alison.
His aunt, the Lady Balcrynie, would receive her
gladly at his request till the day of their marriage.
Let her but tryst with him at the hour and place
he named, and he would carry her straight to

Balcrynie, where she would be safe and happy.
He named that hour, he said, to escape men's
observation for the sake of her own good name.
He named that place, for it was near her dwelling, and on the road between Balcrynie and Heriotside, which fords the Sker Burn. The temptation
was more than mortal heart could resist. She
gave him the promise he sought, stifling the voice
of conscience ; and as she clung to his neck it
seemed to her that heaven was a poor thing compared with a man's love.

Three days remained till Beltane's Eve, and
throughout the time it was noted that Heriotside behaved like one possessed. It may be that
his conscience pricked him, or that he had a glimpse
of his sin and its coming punishment. Certain
it is that, if he had been daft before, he now ran
wild in his pranks, and an evil report of him was
in every mouth. He drank deep at the Cross
Keys, and fought two battles with young lads
that had angered him. One he let off with a
touch on the shoulder, the other goes lame to
this day from a wound he got in the groin. There
was word of the procurator-fiscal taking note of
his doings, and, troth, if they had continued long
he must have fled the country. For a wager
he rode his horse down the Dow Craig, wherefore
the name of the place is the Horseman's Craig
to this day. He laid a hundred guineas with
the laird of Slipperfield that he would drive four
horses through the Slipperfield loch, and in the
prank he had his bit chariot dung to pieces and

a good mare killed. And all men observed that his eyes were wild and his face grey and thin, and that his hand would twitch as he held the glass, like one with the palsy.

The eve of Beltane was lown and hot in the low country, with fire hanging in the clouds and thunder grumbling about the heavens. It seems that up in the hills it had been an awesome deluge of rain, but on the coast it was still dry and lowering. It is a long road from Heriotside to the Skerburnfoot. First you go down the Heriot Water, and syne over the Lang Muir to the edge of Muckle-whan. When you pass the steadings of Mirehope and Cockmalane you turn to the right and ford the Mire Burn. That brings you on to the turn-pike road, which you will ride till it bends inland, when you keep on straight over the Whinny Knowes to the Sker Bay. There, if you are in luck, you will find the tide out and the place fordable dryshod for a man on a horse. But if the tide runs, you will do well to sit down on the sands and content yourself till it turn, or it will be the solans and scarts of the Solloway that will be seeing the next of you.

On this Beltane's Eve the young man, after supping with some wild young blades, bade his horse be saddled about ten o'clock. The company were eager to ken his errand, but he waved them back. "Bide here," he says, "and birl the wine till I return. This is a ploy of my own on which no man follows me." And there was that in his face as he spoke which chilled the wildest, and left them well content to keep to the good claret and the soft seat and let the daft laird go his own ways.

Well and on, he rode down the bridle-path in the wood, along the top of the Heriot glen, and as he rode he was aware of a great noise beneath him. It was not wind, for there was none, and it was not the sound of thunder, and aye as he speired at himself what it was it grew the louder till he came to a break in the trees. And then he saw the cause, for Heriot was coming down in a furious flood, sixty yards wide, tearing at the roots of the aiks, and flinging red waves against the drystone dykes. It was a sight and sound to solemnize a man's mind, deep calling unto deep, the great waters of the hills running to meet with the great waters of the sea. But Heriotside recked nothing of it, for his heart had but one thought and the eye of his fancy one figure. Never had he been so filled with love of the lass, and yet it was not happiness but a deadly secret fear.

As he came to the Lang Muir it was geyan dark, though there was a moon somewhere behind the clouds. It was little he could see of the road, and ere long he had tried many moss-pools and sloughs, as his braw new coat bare witness. Aye in front of him was the great hill of Mucklewhan, where the road turned down by the Mire. The noise of the Heriot had not long fallen behind him ere another began, the same eerie sound of burns crying to ither in the darkness. It seemed that the whole earth was overrun with waters. Every little runnel in the bog was astir, and yet the land around him was as dry as flax, and no drop of rain had fallen. As he rode on the din grew louder, and as he came over the top of Mirehope he kenned by the mighty rushing noise that something uncommon was happening with the Mire Burn. The light from Mirehope sheiling twinkled on his left, and had the man not been dozened with his fancies he might have observed that the steading was deserted and men were crying below in the fields. But he rode on, thinking of but one thing, till he came to the cot-house of Cockmalane, which is nigh the fords of the Mire.

John Dodds, the herd who bode in the place, was standing at the door, and he looked to see who was on the road so late.

"Stop," says he, "stop, Laird Heriotside. I kenna what your errand is, but it is to no holy purpose that ye're out on Beltane Eve. D'ye no hear the warning o' the waters?"

And then in the still night came the sound of Mire like the clash of armies.

"I must win over the ford," says the laird quietly, thinking of another thing.

"Ford!" cried John in scorn. "There'll be nae ford for you the nicht unless it be the ford o' the river Jordan. The burns are up, and bigger than man ever saw them. It'll be a Beltane's Eve that a' folk will remember. They tell me that Gled valley is like a loch, and that there's an awesome folk drooned in the hills. Gin ye were ower the Mire, what about crossin' the Caulds

and the Sker ? " says he, for he jaloused he was
going to Gledsmuir.

And then it seemed that that word brought the
laird to his senses. He looked the airt the rain
was coming from, and he saw it was the airt the
Sker flowed. In a second, he has told me, the
works of the devil were revealed to him. He saw
himself a tool in Satan's hands, he saw his tryst
a device for the destruction of the body, as it was
assuredly meant for the destruction of the soul,
and there came on his mind the picture of an
innocent lass borne down by the waters with no
place for repentance. His heart grew cold in his
breast. He had but one thought, a sinful and
reckless one—to get to her side, that the two
might go together to their account. He heard
the roar of the Mire as in a dream, and when
John Dodds laid hands on his bridle he felled him
to the earth. And the next seen of it was the
laird riding the floods like a man possessed.

The horse was the grey stallion he aye rode,
the very beast he had ridden for many a wager
with the wild lads of the Cross Keys. No man
but himself durst back it, and it had lamed many
a hostler lad and broke two necks in its day. But
it seemed it had the mettle for any flood, and took
the Mire with little spurring. The herds on the
hillside looked to see man and steed swept into
eternity ; but though the red waves were breaking
about his shoulders and he was swept far down,
he aye held on for the shore. The next thing the
watchers saw was the laird struggling up the far

bank, and casting his coat from him, so that he rode in his sark. And then he set off like a wildfire across the muir towards the turnpike road.

Two men saw him on the road and have recorded their experience. One was a gangrel, by name M'Nab, who was travelling from Gledsmuir to Allerkirk with a heavy pack on his back and a bowed head. He heard a sound like wind afore him, and, looking up, saw coming down the road a grey horse stretched out to a wild gallop and a man on its back with a face like a soul in torment. He kenned not whether it was devil or mortal, but flung himself on the roadside, and lay like a corp for an hour or more till the rain aroused him. The other was one Sim Doolittle, the fish hawker from Allerfoot, jogging home in his fish cart from Gledsmuir fair. He had drunk more than was fit for him, and he was singing some light song, when he saw approaching, as he said, the pale horse mentioned in the Revelations, with Death seated as the rider. Thoughts of his sins came on him like a thunderclap, fear loosened his knees, he leaped from the cart to the road, and from the road to the back of a dyke. Thence he flew to the hills, and was found the next morning far up among the Mire Craigs, while his horse and cart were gotten on the Aller sands, the horse lamed and the cart without the wheels.

At the tollhouse the road turns inland to Gledsmuir, and he who goes to Sker Bay must leave it and cross the wild land called the Whinny Knowes, a place rough with bracken and foxes' holes and old stone cairns. The tollman, John Gilzean, was opening his window to get a breath of air in the lown night when he heard or saw the approaching horse. He kenned the beast for Heriotside's, and, being a friend of the laird's, he ran down in all haste to open the yett, wondering to himself about the laird's errand on this night. A voice came down the road to him bidding him hurry; but John's old fingers were slow with the keys, and so it happened that the horse had to stop, and John had time to look up at the gash and woeful face.

"Where away the nicht sae late, laird?" says John.

"I go to save a soul from hell," was the answer.

And then it seems that through the open door there came the chapping of a clock.

"Whatna hour is that?" asks Heriotside.

"Midnicht," says John, trembling, for he did not like the look of things.

There was no answer but a groan, and horse and man went racing down the dark hollows of the Whinny Knowes.

How he escaped a broken neck in that dreadful place no man will ever tell. The sweat, he has told me, stood in cold drops upon his forehead; he scarcely was aware of the saddle in which he sat; and his eyes were stelled in his head, so that he saw nothing but the sky ayont him. The night was growing colder, and there was a small sharp wind stirring from the east. But, hot or cold, it was all one to him, who was already cold as death.

He heard not the sound of the sea nor the pees-
weeps startled by his horse, for the sound that
ran in his ears was the roaring Sker Water and a
girl's cry. The thought kept goading him, and he
spurred the grey till the creature was madder than
himself. It leaped the hole which they call the
Devil's Mull as I would step over a thistle, and
the next he kenned he was on the edge of the
Sker Bay.

It lay before him white and ghastly, with mist
blowing in wafts across it and a slow swaying of
the tides. It was the better part of a mile wide,
but save for some fathoms in the middle where
the Sker current ran, it was no deeper even at
flood than a horse's fetlocks. It looks eerie at
bright midday when the sun is shining and whaups
are crying among the seaweeds ; but think what
it was on that awesome night with the powers of
darkness brooding over it like a cloud. The rider's
heart quailed for a moment in natural fear. He
stepped his beast a few feet in, still staring afore
him like a daft man. And then something in the
sound or the feel of the waters made him look
down, and he perceived that the ebb had begun
and the tide was flowing out to sea.

He kenned that all was lost, and the knowledge
drove him to stark despair. His sins came in his
face like birds of night, and his heart shrank like
a pea. He knew himself for a lost soul, and all
that he loved in the world was out in the tides.
There, at any rate, he could go too, and give back
that gift of life he had so blackly misused. He

cried small and soft like a bairn, and drove the
grey out into the waters. And aye as he spurred
it the foam should have been flying as high as his
head ; but in that uncanny hour there was no
foam, only the waves running sleek like oil. It
was not long ere he had come to the Sker channel,
where the red moss-waters were roaring to the
sea, an ill place to ford in midsummer heat, and
certain death, as folks reputed it, at the smallest
spate. The grey was swimming, but it seemed
the Lord had other purposes for him than death,
for neither man nor horse could drown. He tried
to leave the saddle, but he could not ; he flung the
bridle from him, but the grey held on, as if some
strong hand were guiding. He cried out upon the
devil to help his own, he renounced his Maker and
his God ; but whatever his punishment, he was
not to be drowned. And then he was silent, for
something was coming down the tide.

It came down as quiet as a sleeping bairn,
straight for him as he sat with his horse breasting
the waters, and as it came the moon crept out of
a cloud and he saw a glint of yellow hair. And
then his madness died away and he was himself
again, a weary and stricken man. He hung down
over the tides and caught the body in his arms,
and then let the grey make for the shallows. He
cared no more for the devil and all his myrmidons,
for he kenned brawly he was damned. It seemed
to him that his soul had gone from him and he
was as toom as a hazel shell. His breath rattled
in his throat, the tears were dried up in his head,

his body had lost its strength, and yet he clung
to the drowned maid as to a hope of salvation.
And then he noted something at which he marvelled dumbly. Her hair was drookit back from
her clay-cold brow, her eyes were shut, but in her
face there was the peace of a child. It seemed
even that her lips were smiling. Here, certes, was
no lost soul, but one who had gone joyfully to
meet her Lord. It may be in that dark hour at
the burn-foot, before the spate caught her, she
had been given grace to resist her adversary and
flung herself upon God's mercy.

And it would seem that it had been granted,
for when he came to the Skerburnfoot there in
the corner sat the weird-wife Alison, dead as a
stone and shrivelled like a heather birn.

For days Heriotside wandered the country or
sat in his own house with vacant eye and trembling hands. Conviction of sin held him like a vice :
he saw the lassie's death laid at his door, her face
haunted him by day and night, and the word of
the Lord dirled in his ears telling of wrath and
punishment. The greatness of his anguish wore
him to a shadow, and at last he was stretched
on his bed and like to perish. In his extremity
worthy Doctor Chrystal went to him unasked and
strove to comfort him. Long, long the good man
wrestled, but it seemed as if his ministrations were
to be of no avail. The fever left his body, and
he rose to stotter about the doors ; but he was
still in his torments, and the mercy-seat was far
from him. At last in the back end of the year

came Mungo Muirhead to Caulds to the autumn
communion, and nothing would serve him but he
must try his hand at this storm-tossed soul.   He
spoke with power and unction, and a blessing came
with his words, the black cloud lifted and showed
a glimpse of grace, and in a little the man had
some assurance of salvation.   He became a pillar
of Christ's Kirk, prompt to check abominations,
notably the sin of witchcraft ; foremost in good
works ; but with it all a humble man, who walked
contritely till his death.   When I came first to
Caulds I sought to prevail upon him to accept the
eldership, but he aye put me by, and when I heard
his tale I saw that he had done wisely.   I mind
him well as he sat in his chair or daundered through
Caulds, a kind word for every one and sage counsel
in time of distress, but withal a severe man to
himself and a crucifier of the body.   It seems that
this severity weakened his frame, for three years
syne come Martinmas he was taken ill with a fever,
and after a week's sickness he went to his account,
where I trust he is accepted.

1901.

V

FOUNTAINBLUE

FOUNTAINBLUE

I

ONCE upon a time, as the story-books say, a boy came over a ridge of hill, from which a shallow vale ran out into the sunset. It was a high, wind-blown country, where the pines had a crook in their backs and the rocks were scarred and bitten with winter storms. But below was the beginning of pastoral. Soft birch woods, shady beeches, meadows where cattle had browsed for generations, fringed the little brown river as it twined to the sea. Farther, and the waves broke on white sands, the wonderful billows of the West which cannot bear to be silent. And between, in a garden wilderness, with the evening flaming in its windows, stood Fountainblue, my little four-square castle which guards the valley and the beaches.

The boy had torn his clothes, scratched his face, cut one finger deeply, and soaked himself with bog-water, but he whistled cheerfully and his eyes were happy. He had had an afternoon of adventure, startling emprises achieved in solitude; assuredly a day to remember and mark with a white stone. And the beginning had been most unpromising. After lunch he had been attired in his best raiment, and, in the misery of a broad white collar, dispatched with his cousins to take tea with the small lady who domineered in Fountainblue. The prospect had pleased him greatly, the gardens fed his fancy, the hostess was an old confederate, and there were sure to be excellent things to eat. But his curious temper had arisen to torment him. On the way he quarrelled with his party, and in a moment found himself out of sympathy with the future. The enjoyment crept out of the prospect. He knew that he did not shine in society, he foresaw an afternoon when he would be left out in the cold and his hilarious cousins treated as the favoured guests. He reflected that tea was a short meal at the best, and that games on a lawn were a poor form of sport. Above all, he felt the torture of his collar and the straitness of his clothes. He pictured the dreary return in the twilight, when the afternoon, which had proved, after all, such a dismal failure, had come to a weary end. So, being a person of impulses, he mutinied at the gates of Fountainblue and made for the hills. He knew he should get into trouble, but trouble, he had long ago found out, was his destiny, and he scorned to avoid it. And now, having cast off the fear of God and man, he would for some short hours do exactly as he pleased.

Half-crying with regret for the delights he had forsworn, he ran over the moor to the craggy hills which had always been forbidden him. When he had climbed among the rocks awe fell upon the desolate little adventurer, and he bewailed his choice. But soon he found a blue hawk's nest, and the possession of a coveted egg inspired him to advance. By-and-by he had climbed so high that he could not return, but must needs scale Stob Ghabhar itself. With a quaking heart he achieved it, and then, in the pride of his heroism, he must venture down the Grey Correi where the wild goats lived. He saw one bearded ruffian, and pursued him with stones, stalking him cunningly till he was out of breath. Then he found odd little spleenwort ferns, which he pocketed, and high up in the rocks a friendly raven croaked his encouragement. And then, when the shadows lengthened, he set off cheerily homewards, hungry, triumphant, and very weary.

All the way home he flattered his soul. In one afternoon he had been hunter and trapper, and what to him were girls' games and pleasant things to eat ? He pictured himself the hardy outlaw, feeding on oatmeal and goat's flesh, the terror and pride of his neighbourhood. Could the little mistress of Fountainblue but see him now, how she would despise his prosaic cousins ! And then, as he descended on the highway, he fell in with his forsaken party.

For a wonder they were in good spirits—so good that they forgot to remind him, in their usual way, of the domestic terrors awaiting him. A man had been there who had told them stories and shown them tricks, and there had been cocoa-nut cake, and Sylvia had a new pony on which they had ridden races. The children were breathless with excitement, very much in love with each other as common sharers in past joys. And as they talked all the colour went out of his afternoon. The blue hawk's egg was cracked, and it looked a stupid, dingy object as it lay in his cap. His rare ferns were crumpled and withered, and who was to believe his stories of Stob Ghabhar and the Grey Correi? He had been a fool to barter ponies and tea and a man who knew tricks for the barren glories of following his own fancy. But at any rate he would show no sign. If he was to be an outlaw, he would carry his outlawry well; so with a catch in his voice and tears in his eyes he jeered at his inattentive companions, upbraiding himself all the while for his folly.

him like a rotten stick in half an hour. I like little Despencer, and I don't care about Maitland; but all the same it is absurd to compare the two, except in love-making."

"Lord, it will be comic," and Clanroyden stretched his long legs and lay back on a cushion. The girls were still chattering beside the fire, and the twilight was fast darkening into evening.

"You dislike Maitland?" he asked, looking up. "Now, I wonder why?"

Durward smiled comically at the ceiling. "Oh, I know I oughtn't to. I know he's supposed to be a man's man, and that it's bad form for a man to say he dislikes him, but I'm honest enough to own to detesting him. I suppose he's great, but he's not great enough yet to compel one to fall down and worship him, and I hate greatness in the making. He goes through the world with his infernal arrogance and expects everybody to clear out of his way. I am told we live in an age of reason, but that fellow has burked reason. He never gives a reason for a thing he does, and if you try to argue he crushes you. He has killed good talk for ever with his confounded rudeness. All the little sophistries and conventions which make life tolerable are so much rubbish to him, and he shows it. The plague of him is that he can never make-believe. He is as hard as iron, and as fierce as the devil, and about as unpleasant. You may respect the sledge-hammer type, but it's confoundedly dull. Why, the man has not the imagination of a rabbit, except in his description

of people he dislikes. I liked him when he said
that Layden reminded him of a dissipated dove,
because I disliked Layden ; but when Freddy Alton
played the fool and people forgave him, because
he was a good sort, Maitland sent him about his
business, saying he had no further use for weak-
lings. He is so abominably cold-blooded and im-
placable that every one must fear him, and yet
most people can afford to despise him. All the
kind simple things of life are shut out of his knowledge. He has no nature, only a heart of stone and
an iron will and a terribly subtle brain. Of course
he is a great man—in a way, but at the best he is
only half a man. And to think that he should
have fallen in love, and be in danger of losing to
Despencer ! It's enough to make one forgive him."

Clanroyden laughed. "I can't think of Despencer. It's too absurd. But, seriously, I wish
I saw Maitland well rid of this mood, married or
cured. That sort of man doesn't take things
easily."

"It reminds one of Theocritus and the Cyclops
in love. Who would have thought to see him up
in this moorland place, running after a girl ? He
doesn't care for sport."

"Do you know that he spent most of his childhood in this glen, and that he *is* keen about sport ?
He is too busy for many holidays, but he once
went with Burton to the Caucasus, and Burton
said the experience nearly killed him. He said
that the fellow was tireless, and as mad and reckless as a boy with nothing to lose."

broken teacups with childish impartiality. His own favourite seat was still there, where, hidden by a tapestry screen, he had quarrelled with Sylvia while their elders gossiped. This sudden flood of memories mellowed him towards the world. He was cordial to Despencer, forbore to think Durward a fool, and answered every one of Mr. Etheridge's many questions. For the first time he felt the success of his life. The old house recalled his childhood, and the sight of Clanroyden, his devoted follower, reminded him of his power. Somehow the wearyful crying for the moon, which had always tortured him, was exchanged for a glow of comfort, a shade of complacency in his haggard soul. . . . And then the sight of Claire dispelled his satisfaction.

Here in this cheerful, homely party of friends he found himself out of place. On state occasions he could acquit himself with credit, for the man had a mind. He could make the world listen to him when he chose, and the choice was habitual. But now his loneliness claimed its lawful consequences, and he longed for the little friendly graces which he had so often despised. Despencer talked of scenery and weather with a tenderness to which this man, who loved nature as he loved little else, was an utter stranger. This elegant and appropriate sentiment would have worried him past endurance, if Claire had not shared it. It was she who told some folk-tale about the Grey Correi with the prettiest hesitancy which showed her feeling. And then the talk drifted to books and

people, flitting airily about their petty world.
Maitland felt himself choked by their accomplishments. Most of the subjects were ones no sane
man would trouble to think of, and yet here were
men talking keenly about trifles and disputing with
nimble-witted cleverness on the niceties of the
trivial. Feeling miserably that he was the only
silent one, he plunged desperately into the stream,
found himself pulled up by Despencer and deftly
turned. The event gave him the feeling of having
been foiled by a kitten.

Angry with the world, angrier with his own
angularity, he waited for the end of the meal.
Times had not changed in this house since he
had been saved by Sylvia from social disgrace.
But when the women left the room he found life
easier. His host talked of sport, and he could
tell him more about Stob Ghabhar than any keeper.
Despencer, victorious at dinner, now listened like
a docile pupil. Durward asked a political question, and the answer came sharp and definite.
Despencer demurred gently, after his fashion.
"Well, but surely—" and a grimly smiling
"What do you know about it?" closed the discussion. The old Maitland had returned for the
moment.

The night was mild and impenetrably dark, and
the fall of waters close at hand sounded like a
remote echo. An open hall door showed that some
of the party had gone out to the garden, and the
men followed at random. A glimmer of white
frocks betrayed the women on the lawn, standing

by the little river which slipped by cascade and glide from the glen to the low pasture-lands. In the featureless dark there was no clue to locality. The place might have been Berkshire or a suburban garden.

Suddenly the scream of some animal came from the near thicket. The women started and asked what it was.

"It was a hill-fox," said Maitland to Claire. "They used to keep me awake at nights on the hill. They come and bark close to your ear and give you nightmare."

The lady shivered. "Thank Heaven for the indoors," she said. "Now, if I had been the daughter of one of your old Donalds of the Isles, I should have known that cry only too well. Wild nature is an excellent background, but give me civilization in front."

Maitland was peering into the wood. "You will find it creep far into civilization if you look for it. There is a very narrow line between the warm room and the savage out-of-doors."

"There are miles of luxuries," the girl cried, laughing. "People who are born in the wrong century have to hunt over half the world before they find their savagery. It is all very tame, but I love the tameness. You may call yourself primitive, Mr. Maitland, but you are the most complex and modern of us all. What would Donald of the Isles have said to politics and the Stock Exchange?"

They had strolled back to the house. "Nevertheless I maintain my belief," said the man. "You call it miles of rampart; I call the division a line, a thread, a sheet of glass. But then, you see, you only know one side, and I only know the other."

"What preposterous affectation!" the girl said, as with a pretty shiver she ran indoors. Maitland stood for a moment looking back at the darkness. Within the firelit hall, with its rugs and little tables and soft chairs, he had caught a glimpse of Despencer smoking a cigarette. As he looked towards the hills he heard the fox's bark a second time, and then somewhere from the black distance came a hawk's scream, hoarse, lonely, and pitiless. The thought struck him that the sad elemental world of wood and mountain was far more truly his own than this cosy and elegant civilization. And, oddly enough, the thought pained him.

III

THE day following was wet and windy, when a fire was grateful, and the hills, shrouded in grey mist, had no attractions. The party read idly in arm-chairs during the morning, and in the afternoon Maitland and Clanroyden went down to the stream-mouth after sea trout. So Despencer remained to talk to Claire, and, having played many games of picquet and grown heartily tired of each other, as tea-time approached they fell to desultory comments on their friends. Maitland was beginning to interest the girl in a new way. Formerly he had been a great person who was sensible enough to admire her, but something remote and unattractive, for whom friendship (much less love) was impossible. But now she had begun to feel his power, his manhood. The way in which other men spoke of him impressed her unconsciously, and she began to ask Despencer questions which were gall and wormwood to that young man. But he answered honestly, after his fashion.

"Isn't he very rich?" she asked. "And I suppose he lives very plainly?"

"Rich as Crœsus, and he sticks in his ugly rooms in the Albany because he never thinks enough about the thing to change. I've been in them once, and you never saw such a place. He's a maniac for fresh air, so they're large enough, but they're littered like a stable with odds and ends of belongings. He must have several thousand books, and yet he hasn't a decent binding among them. He hasn't a photograph of a single soul, and only one picture, which, I believe, was his father. But you never saw such a collection of whips and spurs and bits. It smells like a harness room, and there you find Maitland, when by any chance he is at home, working half the night and up to the eyes in papers. I don't think the man has any expenses except food and rent, for he wears the same clothes for years. And he has given up horses."

"Was he fond of horses?" Claire asked.

"Oh, you had better ask him. I really can't tell you any more about him."

"But how do his friends get on with him?"

"He has hardly any, but his acquaintances, who are all the world, say he is the one great man of the future. If you want to read what people think of him, you had better look at the *Monthly*."

Under cover of this one ungenerous word Despencer made his escape, for he hated the business, but made it the rule of his life "never to crab a fellow." Claire promptly sought out the *Monthly*, and found twenty pages of superfine analysis and bitter, grudging praise. She read it with interest and then lay back in her chair and tried to fix her thoughts. It is only your unhealthy young woman who worships strength in the abstract, and the girl tried to determine whether she admired the man as a power or disliked him as a brute. She chose a compromise, and the feeling which survived was chiefly curiosity.

The result of the afternoon was that when the fishermen returned, and Maitland, in dry clothes, appeared for tea, she settled herself beside him and prepared to talk. Maitland being healthily tired, was in an excellent temper, and he found himself enticed into what for him was a rare performance—talk about himself. They were sitting apart from the others, and, ere ever he knew, he was answering the girl's questions with an absent-minded frankness. In a little she had drawn from him the curious history of his life, which most men knew, but never from his own lips.

"I was at school for a year," he said, "and then my father died and our affairs went to pieces. I had to come back and go into an office, a sort of bank. I hated it, but it was good for me, for it taught me something, and my discontent made me ambitious. I had about eighty pounds a year, and I saved from that. I worked too at books incessantly, and by-and-by I got an Oxford scholarship at an obscure college. I went up there, and found myself in a place where every one seemed well-off, while I was a pauper. However, it didn't trouble me much, for I had no ambition to play the fool. I only cared about two things—horses and metaphysics. I hated all games, which I thought only fit for children. I dare say it was foolish, but then you see I had had a queer up-bringing. I managed to save a little money, and one vacation when I was wandering about in Norfolk, sleeping under haystacks and working in harvest fields when my supplies ran down, I came across a farmer. He was a good fellow and a sort of sportsman, and I took a fancy to him. He had a colt to sell which I fancied more, for I saw it had blood in it. So I bought it for what seemed a huge sum to me in those days, but I kept it at his farm and I superintended its education. I broke it myself and taught it to jump, and by-and-by in my third year I brought it to Oxford and entered for the Grind on it. People laughed at me, but I knew my own business. The little boys who rode in the thing knew nothing about horses, and not one in ten could ride; so I entered and won. It was all I wanted, for I could sell my horse then, and the fellow who rode second bought it. It was decent of him, for I asked a big figure, and I think he had an idea of doing me a kindness. I made him my private secretary the other day."

"You mean Lord Drapier?" she asked.

"Yes—Drapier. That gave me money to finish off and begin in town. Oh, and I had got a first in my schools. I knew very little about anything except metaphysics, and I never went to tutors. I suppose I knew a good deal more than the examiners in my own subject, and anyhow they felt

obliged to give me my first after some grumbling.
Then I came up to town with just sixty pounds
in my pocket, but I had had the education of a
gentleman."

Maitland looked out of the window, and the
sight of the mist-clad hills recalled him to himself.
He wondered why he was telling the girl this story,
and he stopped suddenly.

" And what did you do in town ? " she asked,
with interest.

" I hung round and kept my eyes open. I
nearly starved, for I put half my capital on a
horse which I thought was safe, and lost it. By-
and-by, quite by accident, I came across a curious
fellow, Ransome—you probably have heard his
name. I met him in some stables where he was
buying a mare, and he took a liking to me. He
made me his secretary, and then, because I liked
hard work, he let me see his business. It was
enormous for the man was a genius after a fashion ;
and I slaved away in his office and down at the
docks for about three years. He paid me just
enough to keep body and soul together and cover
them with clothes ; but I didn't grumble, for I
had a sort of idea that I was on my probation.
And then my apprenticeship came to an end."

" Yes," said the girl.

" Yes ; for you see Ransome was an odd character. He had a sort of genius for finance, and
within his limits he was even a great adminis-
trator. But in everything else he was as simple
as a child. His soul was idyllic : he loved green

fields and Herrick and sheep. So it had always
been his fancy to back out some day and retire
with his huge fortune to some country place and
live as he pleased. It seemed that he had been
training me from the first day I went into the
business, and now he cut the rope and left the
whole enormous concern in my hands. I needed
every atom of my wits, and the first years were
a hard struggle. I became of course very rich;
but I had to do more, I had to keep the thing
at its old level. I had no natural turn for the
work, and I had to acquire capacity by sheer
grind. However, I managed it, and then, when
I felt my position sure, I indulged myself with a
hobby and went into politics."

"You call it a hobby?"

"Certainly. The ordinary political career is
simply a form of trifling. There's no trade on
earth where a man has to fear so few able com-
petitors. Of course it's very public and honour-
able and that sort of thing, and I like it; but
sometimes it wearies me to death."

The girl was looking at him with curious interest. "Do you always get what you want?"
she asked.

"Never," he said.

"Then is your success all disappointment?"

"Oh, I generally get a bit of my ambitions,
which is all one can hope for in this world."

"I suppose your ambitions are not idyllic,
like Mr. Ransome's?"

He laughed. "No, I suppose not. I never

A little later she came out with a bundle of letters in her hands. "Here are your letters, Mr. Maitland; but you mustn't try to answer them, or you'll be late." He put the lot in his jacket pocket and looked up at the laughing girl. "My work is six hundred miles behind me," he said, "and to-day I have only the Eilean na Cille to think of." And, as she passed by, another name took the place of the Eilean, and it seemed to him that at last he had found the link which was to bind together the two natures—his boyhood and his prime.

Out on the loch the sun was beating with that steady August blaze which is more torrid than midsummer. But as the yacht slipped between the horns of the land, it came into a broken green sea with rollers to the north where the tireless Atlantic fretted on the reefs. In a world of cool salt winds and the golden weather of afternoon, with the cries of tern and gull about the bows and the foam and ripple of green water in the wake, the party fell into a mood of supreme contentment. The restless Claire was stricken into a figure of contemplation, which sat in the bows and watched the hazy blue horizon and the craggy mainland hills in silent delight. Maitland was revelling in the loss of his isolation. He had ceased to be alone, a leader, and for the moment felt himself one of the herd, a devotee of humble pleasures. His mind was blank, his eyes filled only with the sea, and the lady of his devotion, in that happy moment of romance, seemed to

have come at last within the compass of his
hopes.

The Islands of the Waves are low green ridges
which rise little above the highest tide-mark.
The grass is stiff with salt, the sparse heather
and rushes are crooked with the winds, but there
are innumerable little dells where a light wild
scrub flourishes, and in one a spring of sweet
water sends a tiny stream to the sea. The yacht's
company came ashore in boats, and tea was made
with a great bustle beside the well, while the men
lay idly in the bent and smoked. All wind seemed
to have died down, a soft, cool, airless peace like
a June evening was abroad, and the heavy surg-
ing of the tides had sunk to a distant whisper.
Maitland lifted his head, sniffed the air, and looked
uneasily to the west, meeting the eye of one of
the sailors engaged in the same scrutiny. He
beckoned the man to him.

"What do you make of the weather?" he
asked.

The sailor, an East-coast man from Arbroath,
shook his head. "It's ower lown a' of a sudden,"
he said. "It looks like mair wind nor we want,
but I think it'll haud till the morn."

Maitland nodded and lay down again. He
smiled at the return of his old sea craft and weather
lore, on which he had prided himself in his boyhood; and when Claire came up to him with tea
she found him grinning vacantly at the sky.

"What a wonderful lull in the wind," she said.
"When I was here last these were real isles of

the waves, with spray flying over them and a great business to land. But now they might be the island in Fountainblue lake."

"Did you ever hear of the Ocean Quiet?" he asked. "I believe it to be a translation of a Gaelic word which is a synonym for death, but it is also a kind of natural phenomenon. Old people at Cairnlora used to talk of it. They said that sometimes fishermen far out at sea in blowing weather came into a place of extraordinary peace, where the whole world was utterly still and they could hear their own hearts beating."

"What a pretty fancy!" said the girl.

"Yes; but it had its other side. The fishermen rarely came home alive, and if they did they were queer to the end of their days. Another name for the thing was the Breathing of God. It is an odd idea, the passing from the wholesome turmoil of nature to the uncanny place where God crushes you by His silence."

"All the things to eat are down by the fire," she said, laughing. "Do you know, if you weren't what you are, people might think you a poet, Mr. Maitland. I thought you cared for none of these things."

"What things?" he asked. "I don't care for poetry. I am merely repeating the nonsense I was brought up on. Shall I talk to you about politics?"

"Heaven forbid! And now I will tell you my own story about these isles. There is a hermit's cell on one of them and crosses, like Iona.

The hermit lived alone all winter, and was fed by
boats from the shore when the weather was calm.
When one hermit died another took his place, and
no one knew where he came from. Now one
day a great lord in Scotland disappeared from
his castle. He was the King's Warden of the
Marches and the greatest soldier of his day, but
he disappeared utterly out of men's sight, and
people forgot about him. Long years after the
Northmen in a great fleet came down upon these
isles, and the little chiefs fled before them. But
suddenly among them there appeared an old man,
the hermit of the Wave Islands, who organized
resistance and gathered a strong army. No one
dared oppose him, and the quarrelsome petty
chiefs forgot their quarrels under his banner, for
he had the air of one born to command. At last
he met the invaders in the valley of Fountainblue,
and beat them so utterly that few escaped to their
ships. He fell himself in the first charge, but not
before his followers had heard his battle-cry of
'Saint Bride,' and known that the Hermit of the
Isles and the great King's Warden were the same."

"That was a common enough thing in wild
times. Men grew tired of murder and glory and
waving banners, and wanted quiet to make their
peace with their own souls. I should have thought
the craving scarcely extinct yet."

"Then here is your chance, Mr. Maitland,"
said the girl, laughing. "A little trouble would
make the hut habitable, and you could simply
disappear, leaving no address to forward your

letters to. Think of the sensation, 'Disappearance
of a Secretary of State,' and the wild theories and
the obituaries. Then some day when the land
question became urgent on the mainland, you
would turn up suddenly, settle it with extraordinary wisdom, and die after confiding your life-
story to some country reporter. But I am afraid
it would scarcely do, for you would be discovered
by Scotland Yard, which would be ignominious."

"It is a sound idea, but the old device is too
crude. However, it could be managed differently.
Some day, when civilization grows oppressive,
Miss Claire, I will remember your advice."

The afternoon shadows were beginning to
lengthen, and from the west a light sharp wind
was crisping the sea. The yacht was getting
up steam, and boats were coming ashore for the
party. The deep blue waters flushed rose-pink
as the level westering sun smote them from the
summit of a cloud-bank. The stillness had gone,
and the air was now full of sounds and colour.
Claire, with an eye on the trim yacht, declared
her disapproval. "It is an evening for the cutter,"
she cried, and in spite of Mrs. Etheridge's protests
she gave orders for it to be made ready. Then
the self-willed young woman looked round for
company. "Will you come, Mr. Maitland?" she
said. "You can sail a boat, can't you? And
Mr. Despencer, I shall want you to talk to me
when Mr. Maitland is busy. We shall race the
yacht, for we ought to be able to get through the
Scart's Neck with this wind."

"I am not sure if you are wise, Miss Claire,"
and Maitland pulled down his brows as he looked
to the west. "It will be wind—in a very little,
and you stand the chance of a wetting."

"I don't mind. I want to get the full good
of such an evening. You want to be near the
water to understand one of our sunsets. I can
be a barbarian too, you know."

It was not for Maitland to grumble at this
friendliness; so he followed her into the cutter
with Despencer, who had no love for the orders
but much for her who gave them. He took the
helm and steered, with directions from the lady,
from his memory of the intricate coast. Despencer with many rugs looked to Claire's comfort, and, having assured his own, was instantly
entranced with the glories of the evening.

The boat tripped along for a little in a dazzle
of light into the silvery grey of the open water.
Far in front lay the narrow gut called the Scart's
Neck, which was the byway to the loch of Fountainblue. Then Maitland at the helm felt the
sheets suddenly begin to strain, and, looking
behind, saw that the Isles of the Waves were
almost lost in the gloom, and that the roseate
heavens were quickly darkening behind. The
wind which he had feared was upon them; a
few seconds more and it was sending the cutter
staggering among billows. He could barely make
himself heard in the din, as he roared directions
to Despencer about disposing of his person in

another part of the boat. The girl, with flushed
face, was laughing in pure joy of the storm. She
caught a glimpse of Maitland's serious eye and
looked over the gunwale at the threatening west.
Then she too became quiet, and meekly sat down
on the thwart to which he motioned her.

The gale made the Scart's Neck impossible,
and the murky sky seemed to promise greater
fury ere the morning. Twilight was falling,
and the other entrance to the quiet loch meant
the rounding of a headland and a difficult course
through a little archipelago. It was the only way,
for return was out of the question, and it seemed
vain to risk the narrow chances of the short cut.
Maitland looked down at his two companions,
and reflected with pleasure that he was the con-
troller of their fates. He had sailed much as a
boy, and he found in this moment of necessity
that his old lore returned to him. He felt no
mistrust of his powers : whatever the gale he
could land them at Fountainblue, though it might
take hours and involve much discomfort. He
remembered the coast like his own name ; he
relished the grim rage of the elements, and he
kept the cutter's head out to sea with a delight
in the primeval conflict.

The last flickering rays of light coming from
the screen of cloud illumined the girl's pale face,
and the sight disquieted him. There was a hint
of tragedy in this game. Despencer, nervously
self-controlled, was reassuring Claire. Plough-
ing onward in the blackening night in a frail

boat on a wind-threshed sea was no work for a
girl. But it was Despencer who was comfort-
ing her! Well, it was his proper work. He
was made for the business of talking soft things
to women. Maitland, his face hard with spray,
looked into the darkness with a kind of humour
in his heart. And then, as the boat shore and
dipped into the storm, its human occupants seemed
to pass out of the picture, and it was only a shell
tossed on great waters in the unfathomable night.
The evening had come, moonless and starless,
and Maitland steered as best he could by the
deeper blackness which was the configuration of
the shore. Something loomed up that he knew
for the headland, and they were drifting in a quieter
stretch of sea, with the breakers grumbling ahead
from the little tangle of islands.

Suddenly he fell into one of the abstractions
which had always dogged him through his stren-
uous life. His mind was clear, he chose his course
with a certain precision, but the winds and waves
had become to him echoes of echoes. Wet with
spray and shifting his body constantly with the
movement of the boat, it yet was all a phantasmal
existence, while his thoughts were following an
airy morrice in a fairyland world. The motto of
his house, the canting motto of old reivers, danced
in his brain—" Parmi ceu haut bois conduyrai
m'amie "—" Through the high wood I will conduct my love "—and in a land of green forests,
dragon-haunted, he was piloting Claire robed in a
quaint mediaeval gown, himself in speckless plate-

armour. His fancy fled through a score of scenes, sometimes on a dark heath, or by a lonely river, or among great mountains, but always the lady and her protector. Claire, looking up from Despencer's side, saw his lips moving, noted that his eyes were glad, and for a moment hoped better things of their chances.

Then suddenly she was numb with alarm, for the cutter heeled over, and but that Maitland woke to clear consciousness and swung the sheet loose, all would have been past. The adventure nerved him and quickened his senses. The boat seemed to move more violently than the wind drove her, and in the utter blackness he felt for the first time the grip of the waters. The ugly cruel monster had wakened, and was about to wreak its anger on the toy. And then he remembered the currents which raced round Eilean Righ and the scattered isles. Dim shapes loomed up, shapes strange and unfriendly, and he felt miserably that he was as helpless now as Despencer. To the left night had wholly shut out the coast ; his one chance was to run for one of the isles and risk a landing. It would be a dreary waiting for the dawn, but safety had come before any comfort. And yet, he remembered, the little islands were rock-bound and unfriendly, and he was hurrying forward in the grip of a black current with a gale behind and unknown reefs before.

And then he seemed to recollect something of this current which swept along the isles. In a little—so he recalled a boyish voyage in clear

weather—they would come to a place where the
sea ran swift and dark beside a kind of natural
wharf. Here he had landed once upon a time,
but it was a difficult enterprise, needing a quick
and a far leap at the proper moment, for the stream
ran very fast. But if this leap were missed there
was still a chance. The isle was the great Eilean
Righ, and the current swung round its southern
end, and then, joining with another stream, turned
up its far side, and for a moment washed the shore.
But if this second chance were missed, then nothing remained but to fall into the great sea-going
stream and be carried out to death in the wide
Atlantic.

He strained his eyes to the right for Eilean Righ.
Something seemed to approach, as they bent under
an access of the gale. They bore down upon it,
and he struggled to keep the boat's head away,
for at this pace to grate upon rock would mean
upsetting. The sail was down, fluttering amid-
ships like a captive bird, and the mast bowed
with the wind. He leaned forward and called to
Claire. She caught his arm like a child, and he
pulled her up beside him. Then he beckoned
Despencer, and, shrieking against the din, told
him to follow him when he jumped. Despencer
nodded, his teeth chattering with cold and the
novel business.

Suddenly out of the darkness, a yard on their
right, loomed a great flat rock along which the
current raced like a mill-lade. The boat made to
strike, but Maitland forced her nose out to sea,

and then as the stern swung round he seized his
chance. Holding Claire with his left arm he stood
up, balanced himself for a moment on the gunwale,
and jumped. He landed sprawling on his side on
some wet seaweed, over which the sea was lipping,
but undeniably on land. As he pulled himself up
he had a vision of the cutter, dancing like a cork,
vanishing down the current into the darkness.

Holding the girl in his arms he picked his way
across the rock pools to the edge of the island
heather. For a moment he thought Claire had
fainted. She lay still and inert, her eyes shut,
her hair falling foolishly over her brow. He
sprinkled some water on her face, and she revived
sufficiently to ask her whereabouts. He was cross-
ing the island to find Despencer, but he did not
tell her. " You are safe," he said, and he carried
her over the rough ground as lightly as a child.
An intense exhilaration had seized him. He ran
over the flats and strode up the low hillocks with
one thought possessing his brain. To save Despencer, that of course was the far-off aim on his
mind's horizon, but all the foreground was filled
with the lady. " Parmi ceu haut bois "—the old
poetry of the world had penetrated to his heart.
The black night and the wild wind and the sea
were the ministrants of love. The hollow shams of
life with their mincing conventions had departed,
and in this savage out-world a man stood for a
man. The girl's light tweed jacket was no match
for this chill gale, so he stopped for a moment,
took off his own shooting-coat and put it round

her. And then, as he came over a little ridge, he was aware of a grumbling of waters and the sea.

The beach was hidden in a veil of surf which sprinkled the very edge of the bracken. Beyond, the dark waters were boiling like a cauldron, for the tides in this little bay ran with the fury of a river in spate. A moon was beginning to struggle through the windy clouds, and surf, rock, and wave began to shape themselves out of the night. Claire stood on the sand, a slim, desolate figure, and clung to Maitland's arm. She was still dazed with the storm and the baffling suddenness of change. Maitland, straining his eyes out to sea, was in a waking dream. With the lady no toil was too great, no darkness terrible; for her he would scale the blue air and plough the hills and do all the lover's feats of romance. And then suddenly he shook her hand roughly from his arm and ran forward, for he saw something coming down the tide.

The cutter swung to the current, an odd amorphous thing, now heeling over with a sudden gust and now pulled back to balance by the strong grip of the water. A figure seemed to sit in the stern, making feeble efforts to steer. Maitland knew the coast and the ways of the sea. He ran through the surf-ring into the oily-black eddies, shouting to Despencer to come overboard. Soon he was not ten yards from the cutter's line, where the current made a turn towards the shore before it washed the iron rocks to the right. He found deep water, and in two strokes was in the grip of the tides and borne wildly towards the reef. He prepared himself for what was coming, raising his feet and turning his right shoulder to the front. And then with a shock he was pinned against the rock wall, with the tides tugging at his legs, while his hands clung desperately to a shelf. Here he remained, yelling directions to the coming boat. Surf was in his eyes, so that at first he could not see, but at last in a dip of the waves he saw the cutter, a man's form in the stern, plunging not twenty yards away. Now was his chance or never, for while the tide would take a boat far from his present place of vantage, it would carry a lighter thing, such as a man's body, in a circle nearer to the shore. He yelled again, and the world seemed to him quiet for a moment, while his voice echoed eerily in the void. Despencer must have heard it, for the next moment he saw him slip pluckily overboard, making the cutter heel desperately with his weight. And then—it seemed an age— a man, choking and struggling weakly, came down the current, and, pushing his right arm out against the rush of water, he had caught the swimmer by the collar and drawn him in to the side of the rock.

Then came the harder struggle. Maitland's left hand was numbing, and though he had a foothold, it was too slight to lean on with full weight. Lassitude oppressed him, a supreme desire to slip into those racing tides and rest. He was in no panic about death, but he had the practical man's love of an accomplished task, and it nerved him to the extreme toil. Slowly by inches he drew himself up the edge of the reef, cherishing jealously each grip and foothold, with Despencer, half-choked and all but fainting, hanging heavily on his right arm. Blind with spray, sick with sea-water, and aching with his labours, he gripped at last the tangles of seaweed, which meant the flat surface, and with one final effort raised himself and Despencer to the top. There he lay for a few minutes with his head in a rock-pool till the first weariness had passed.

He staggered with his burden in his arms along the ragged reef to the strip of sand where Claire was weeping hysterically. The sight of her restored Maitland to vigour, the appeal of her lonely figure there in the wet bracken. She must think them all dead, he reflected, and herself desolate, for she could not have interpreted rightly his own wild rush into the waves. When she heard his voice she started, as if at a ghost, and then seeing his burden, ran towards him. "Oh, he is dead!" she cried. "Tell me! tell me!" and she clasped the inert figure so that her arm crossed Maitland's. Despencer, stupefied and faint, was roused to consciousness by a woman's kisses on his cheek, and still more by his bearer abruptly laying him on the heather. Claire hung over him like a mother, calling him by soft names, pushing his hair from his brow, forgetful of her own wet and sorry plight. And meanwhile Maitland stood watching, while his palace of glass was being shivered about his ears.

Aforetime his arrogance had kept him from any thought of jealousy; now the time and place were too solemn for trifling, and facts were laid bare before him. Sentiment does not bloom readily in a hard nature, but if it once comes to flower it does not die without tears and agonies. The wearied man, who stood quietly beside the hysterical pair, had a moment of peculiar anguish. Then he conquered sentiment, as he had conquered all other feelings of whose vanity he was assured. He was now, as he was used to be, a man among children; and as a man he had his work. He bent over Claire. " I know a hollow in the middle of the island," he said, " where we can camp the night. I'll carry Despencer, for his ankle is twisted. Do you think you could try to walk ? "

The girl followed obediently, her eyes only on her lover. Her trust in the other was infinite, her indifference to him impenetrable; while he, hopelessly conscious of his fate, saw in the slim dishevelled figure at his side the lost lady, the mistress for him of all romance and generous ambitions. The new springs in his life were choked; he had still his work, his power, and, thank God, his courage; but the career which ran out to the horizon of his vision was bleak and loveless. And he held in his arms the thing which had frustrated him, the thing he had pulled out of the deep in peril of his body; and at the thought life for a moment seemed to be only a comic opera with tragedy to shift the scenes.

He found a cleft between two rocks with a soft floor of heather. There had been no rain, so the bracken was dry, and he gathered great armfuls and driftwood logs from the shore. Soon he had a respectable pile of timber, and then in the nick of the cleft he built a fire. His matches, being in his jacket pocket, had escaped the drenchings of salt water, and soon with a smoke and crackling and sweet scent of burning wood, a fire was going cheerily in the darkness. Then he made a couch of bracken, and laid there the still feeble Despencer. The man was more weak than ill; but for his ankle he was unhurt; and a little brandy would have brought him to himself. But this could not be provided, and Claire saw in his condition only the sign of mortal sickness. With haggard eyes she watched by him, easing his head, speaking soft kind words, forgetful of her own cold and soaking clothes. Maitland drew her gently to the fire, shook down the bracken to make a rest for her head, and left a pile of logs ready for use. " I am going to the end of the island," he said, " to light a fire for a signal. It is the only part which they can see from the mainland, and if they see the blaze they will come off for us as soon as it is day." The pale girl listened obediently. This man was the master, and in his charge was the safety of her lover and herself.

Maitland turned his back upon the warm nook, and stumbled along the ridge to the northern extremity of the isle. It was not half a mile away, but the land was so rough with gullies and crags that the journey took him nearly an hour. Just off the extreme point was a flat rock, sloping northward to a considerable height, a place from

V

MR. HENRY DURWARD TO LADY
CLAUDIA ETHERIDGE

" . . . THINGS have happened, my dear Clo,
since I last wrote; time has passed;
to-morrow I leave this place and go to stalk with
Drapier; and yet in the stress of departure I
take time to answer the host of questions with
which you assailed me. I am able to give you
the best of news. You have won your bet. Your
prophecy about the conduct of the ' other Etheridge girl ' has come out right. They are both
here, as it happens, having come on from Fountainblue—both the hero and the heroine, I mean,
of this most reasonable romance. You know
Jack Despencer, one of the best people in the
world, though a trifle given to chirping. But
I don't think the grasshopper will become a burden to Miss Claire, for she likes that sort of thing.
She must, for there is reason to believe that she
refused for its sake the greatest match—I speak
with all reverence—which this happy country
could offer. I know you like Maitland as little

as I do, but we agree in admiring the Colossus
from a distance. Well, the Colossus has, so to
speak, been laid low by a frivolous member of
your sex. It is all a most romantic tale. Probably you have heard the gist of it, but here is
the full and circumstantial account.

*　　　*　　　*　　　*　　　*　　　*

" We found Maitland beside the fire he had
been feeding all night, and I shall never forget
his figure alone in the dawn on that rock, drenched
and dishevelled, but with his haggard white face
set like a Crusader's. He took us to a kind of
dell in the centre of the island, where we found
Claire and Despencer shivering beside a dying
fire. He had a twisted ankle and had got a bad
scare, while she was perfectly composed, though
she broke down when we got home. It must
have been an awful business for both, but Maitland never seems to have turned a hair. I want
to know two things. First, how in the presence
of great danger he managed to get his dismissal
from the lady—for get it he assuredly did, and
Despencer at once appeared in the part of the
successful lover ; second, what part he played
in the night's events. Claire remembered little,
Despencer only knew that he had been pulled
out of the sea, but over all Maitland seems to
have brooded like a fate. As usual he told us
nothing. It was always his way to give the world
results and leave it to find out his methods for
itself. . . .

" Despencer overwhelmed him with gratitude.

His new happiness made him in love with life, and he included Maitland in the general affection. The night's events seemed to have left their mark on the great man also. He was very quiet, forgot to be rude to anybody, and was kind to both Claire and Despencer. It is his way of acknowledging defeat, the great gentleman's way, for, say what we like about him, he is a tremendous gentleman, one of the last of the breed. . . .

"And then he went away—two days later. Just before he went Hugh Clanroyden and myself were talking in the library, which has a window opening on a flower garden. Despencer was lying in an invalid's chair under a tree and Claire was reading to him. Maitland was saying good-bye, and he asked for Despencer. We told him that he was with Claire in the garden. He smiled one of those odd scarce smiles of his and went out to them. When I saw his broad shoulders bending over the chair and the strong face looking down at the radiant Jack with his amiable good looks, confound it, Clo, I had to contrast the pair, and admit with Shakespeare the excellent foppery of the world. Well-a-day! 'Smooth Jacob still robs homely Esau.' And perhaps it is a good thing, for we are most of us Jacobs, and Esau is an uncomfortable fellow in our midst.

"A week later came the surprising, the astounding news that he had taken the African Governorship. A career ruined, every one said, the finest chance in the world flung away; and then people speculated, and the story came out

in bits, and there was only one explanation. It
is the right one, as I think you will agree, but it
points to some hidden weakness in that iron soul
that he could be moved to fling over the ambitions of years because of a girl's choice. He will
go and bury himself in the wilds, and our party
will have to find another leader. Of course he
will do his work well, but it is just as if I were
to give up my chances of the Woolsack for a
county-court judgeship. He will probably be
killed, for he has a million enemies ; he is perfectly
fearless, and he does not understand the arts of
compromise. It was a privilege, I shall always
feel, to have known him. He was a great man,
and yet—intellect, power, character, were at the
mercy of a girl's caprice. As I write, I hear
Claire's happy laugh below in the garden, probably at some witticism of the fortunate Jack's.
Upon which, with my usual pride in the obvious,
I am driven to reflect that the weak things in
life may confound the strong, and that, after
all, the world is to the young. . . ."

VI

SIR HUGH CLANROYDEN TO MR. HENRY DURWARD. SOME YEARS LATER

" . . . I AM writing this on board ship, as you will see from the heading, and shall post it when I get to Port Said. You have heard of my appointment, and I need not tell you how deep were my searchings of heart before I found courage to accept. Partly I felt that I had got my chance ; partly I thought—an inconsequent feeling—that Maitland, if he had lived, would have been glad to see me in the place. But I am going to wear the giant's robe, and Heaven knows I have not the shoulders to fill it. Yet I am happy in thinking that I am in a small sense faithful to his memory.

" No further news, I suppose, has come of the manner of his death ? Perhaps we shall never know, for it was on one of those expeditions with a few men by which he held the frontier. I wonder if any one will ever write fully the history of all that he did ? It must have been a titanic work, but his methods were always so quiet that people accepted his results like a gift from Providence. He was given, one gathers, a practically free hand, and he made the country—four years' work of a man of genius. They wished to bring his body home, but he made them bury him where he fell—a characteristic last testament. And so he has gone out of the world into the world's history.

"I am still broken by his death, but, now that he is away, I begin to see him more clearly. Most people, I think, misunderstood him. I was one of his nearest friends, and I only knew bits of the man. For one thing—and I hate to use the vulgar word—he was the only aristocrat I ever heard of. Our classes are three-fourths of them of yesterday's growth, without the tradition, character, manner, or any trait of an aristocracy. And the few, who are nominally of the blood, have gone to seed in mind, or are spoilt by coarse marriages, or, worst of all, have the little trifling superior airs of incompetence. But he, he had the most transcendent breeding in mind and spirit. He had no need for self-assertion, for his most casual acquaintances put him at once in a different class from all other men. He had never a trace of a vulgar ideal; men's opinions, worldly honour, the common pleasures of life, were merely degrees of the infinitely small. And yet he was no bloodless mystic. If race means anything, he had it to perfection. Dreams and fancies to him were the realities, while facts were the shadows which he made dance as it pleased him.

" The truth is, that he was that rarest of mortals, the iron dreamer. He thought in æons and cosmic cycles, and because of it he could do what he pleased in life. We call a man practical if he is struggling in the crowd with no knowledge of his whereabouts, and yet in our folly we deny the name to the clear-sighted man who can rule the crowd from above. And here I join issue with you and everybody else. You thought it was Claire's refusal which sent him abroad and interrupted his career. I read the thing otherwise. His love for the girl was a mere accident, a survival of the domestic in an austere spirit. Something, I do not know what, showed him his true desires. She may have rejected him ; he may never have spoken to her ; in any case the renunciation had to come. You must remember that that visit to Fountainblue was the first that he had paid since his boyhood to his boyhood's home. Those revisitings have often a strange trick of self-revelation. I believe that in that night on the island he saw our indoor civilization and his own destiny in so sharp a contrast that he could not choose but make the severance. He found work where there could be small hope of honour or reward, but many a chance for a hero. And I am sure that he was happy, and that it was the longed-for illumination that dawned on him with the bullet which pierced his heart.

" But, you will say, the fact remains that he was once in love with Claire, and that she would have none of him. I do not deny it. He was never a favourite with women ; but, thank Heaven, I have better things to do than study their peculiarities. . . ."

1901.

THE END

PRINTED IN GREAT BRITAIN AT
THE PRESS OF THE PUBLISHERS